THE
PROPOSITION

RAMIN HOODEH

Ramin Vision Publishing
Ltd.

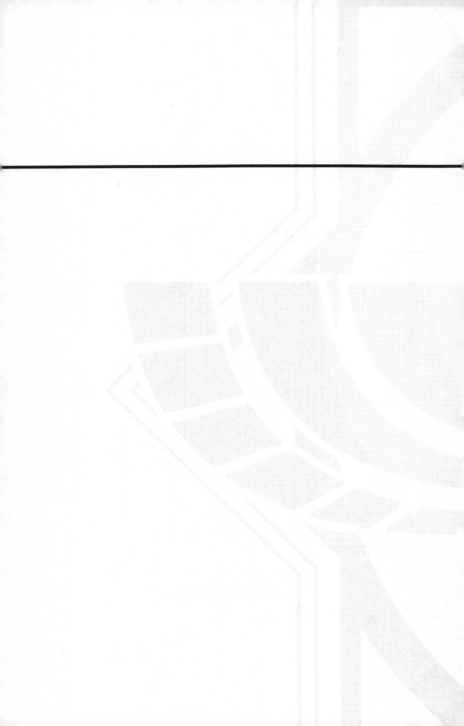

"A LITTLE BIT OF KNOWLEDGE

CAN BE A DANGEROUS THING;

OR IT CAN BE A VIBRANT SEED

GIVING RISE TO VERDANT FORESTS

AND AWAKENING SLEEPING GIANTS."

- CHAN THOMAS -

For those who enjoy reading with a little bit of background music. Here is a recommendation for this story:

author.vision/ambience

CHAPTER

1

A long time ago, Ali had found himself lost, desolate and trapped in the confines of a cold, dark prison cell. Boredom wasn't stillness; boredom was sameness. Ali's life had become an infinite stream of cyclical monotony; no day was any different from the other, and there was no prospect that the day after would differ from the last. Ali craved stimulus, even of the adverse kind. For even conflict would inject some life into him, and resuscitate the purpose of his remaining years.

Ali, a diplomatic writer and a loving husband and father, was captured and sentenced to life as a prisoner of war. His sole crime? Existing in a country under political turmoil. Shackled to a tedious fate, Ali's only companion was a silent prison guard, employed with the duty of feeding him enough to sustain his withering frame for just another day. This modicum of mercy was no usual treat for a political prisoner. But Ali was no usual prisoner.

We must bear in mind that Ali was an ardent scholar, revered throughout the entire Middle East for his revelatory way with words. He was a man of great personal integrity who devoted his life to the quest for truth. And with every fragment of truth he uncovered, he served to enlighten his people during a time when the truth had been subjugated. This was his lifeline. His allegiance to the truth surely saved him from a near mortal fate, for even the most heartless of adversaries knew that Ali's mind was too valuable to waste.

Each day, the prison guard would attend Ali's cell and leave two piles of documents at his feet; one pile of old scriptures ready to be translated, and a second pile of blank pages, fresh for him to write on. This was Ali's work. It helped keep his mind stimulated throughout the hourless days. For this he was eternally thankful, as the texts he received boasted a peculiar depth, with topics ranging from geo-politics, history, science, religious and Vedic texts. There were even cryptic Egyptian manuscripts and esoteric Biblical stories, an entire myriad of subject matters inexhaustible. These were an insatiable mystery to Ali.

But whenever he quizzed the prison guard as to what the source of these texts were? What was their purpose? And for whom he was translating them for? His questions were sorely met with stony silence.

One night, before Ali surrendered to the lull of sleep, he pondered upon the words he had written as they reverberated amidst his thoughts. "Is this how my fate will end? Is this all there is?" he thought, staring vacantly into the ceiling. Frustrated and depleted, he fell into a deep slumber and started to dream. He stumbled into the great infinite nothingness, cascading into the endless void of night, and sang silently toward the sky:

"For uncounted years I have tried to grasp the meaning of my existence. How many more years am I destined to reach you and become whole?

Where are you, my light? Show me the path towards your truth, I am a moth searching for your flame. Please my Lord, do not let me die in vain.

The harder I try, the further I become from you... your purity and beauty.

But how can I not ask, how could I not search? Let your beauty fill my eye.

For eternity I will pray, forever from today. To know the great truth; the truth of myself, of my mind, tell me the purpose of the life I painfully left behind."

And on that night, in the cold prison cell, while Ali contemplated the wonders of life and the mysteries of the Universe, a great light descended upon him. Mesmerising and iridescent, a magnificent outline of a woman gently emerged. Familiar and roguelike, Hypatia of Alexandria radiant, hallowed and all stupendous, she gazed toward him adoringly, her voice permeating the depths of his mind:

"My dear Ali,

I am the one you have served.
Now you are in need,
I will serve you."

CHAPTER

2

A li slowly awoke that morning, the dawn glow accompanying him as he roused ever so gently. His eyes, refusing to cooperate, remained stapled shut, desperate to savour what his memory tried to efface.

"Salma... was that... you?" he thought. "No, that can't be...".

"ALI" the prison guard's voice shrilled through the prison hallway. Although startled, Ali welcomed the sight of the guard as he unlocked his cell, curious as to why the guard was paying a visit at such an irregular hour.

The guard gestured towards him, confronting him this time with just one single sheet of paper and a pen in the other hand.

"What is this?" asked Ali "Have I made some sort of mistake?"

"Sign this... This is your way out" instructed the guard.

"You're letting me go? Why? Is the war over?"

"No, the scriptures you translated from the Vatican archives have proven very useful for our intelligence agency. The Ministry have taken a liking to your work, and would like you to join them full time, effective immediately."

Ali was perplexed, completely taken aback by the multitude of news he'd received. "What?!" he yelled "You mean to tell me that I've been serving your intelligence agency this whole time? Was that the purpose of the translations?"

"I don't know the full details."

"But why texts from the Vatican? What good are these religious stories to a government agency anyway?"

The guard laughed, "If you sign the papers and join us, you'll find out soon enough...Why hesitate? Don't you want to get out of here and claim your liberty?"

Ali felt sickened at the mere thought "Join you?" he replied "I'd rather die than work for the army of the devil!"

"It's not like you have a choice, Ali. Don't make this any harder than it needs to be."

"If I knew my translations would be used for nefarious means, I wouldn't have written a single word. Get away from me, you artful spirit! Tell your evil Ministers I demand to be killed or left alone!"

The guard's expression turned to stone, "I said you don't want to make this any more difficult... As a gesture of mercy, I'll let you sleep on it. We can repeat this same facade tomorrow morning but on the premise that we have your full cooperation. This part is non-negotiable. Please, cooperate Ali. Just... don't do this to yourself."

The guard walked towards the cell door before stopping, well-timed in his faith of Ali's response.

"I know you don't enjoy speaking like that, young man" mustered Ali "you don't believe in what you are forced to say to me."

The guard let out a deep sigh "I'm just doing my job" he said, reaching to close the cell door behind him. Before closing it he turned toward Ali, his gaze dropped to the floor. He stood still in the doorway, and he couldn't help but say:

"Ali... I have been ordered not to speak to you, for reasons I cannot disclose. But, every day, I watch you writing, so intently.. and for months I have longed to ask you about your work, your books and enquire about your mind. You look at me like I am the spawn of Satan, your Adversary, but I am not the one who imprisoned you. I am not too bad a person. I am also a father. I work hard to bring a salary home each month to take care of my wife, my mother and my children... I am destined to a definite fate not dissimilar to yours," the guard deliberated, justifying himself to a dismissive Ali. "And as your only, albeit, silent companion, it would pain me to see you wither away in this cell... Accept this Proposition. Please. Do not condemn your life to hell."

He stared expectantly at Ali, but was met with silence.

"... Okay, Ali. Suit yourself... But I expect a different outcome when I come back tomorrow. Your life depends on it."

He walked away closing the cell door behind him, disappointed, until finally, he gained a response.

"You and me are not alike, young man," said Ali, his voice piercing through the echo of the stone chamber, "you say that you feed your family, but it is with the blood of the innocent that you fill their cup. You, who are free to leave your deeply funded, developed country, have chosen to be the henchman of the beast. You say your fate is akin to mine, but you do not know of the pain I have been through. You, a pawn of the puppet, have only met me at the devil's door. And while you were sleeping peacefully on a summer's night, I was fleeing my home from your invading army."

The guard, disturbed and defensive, silently absorbed the reality of Ali's harsh words. Hoping to develop some rapport with him, he asked "Ali, will you tell me... what happened to you?"

"I don't want to talk about it," Ali replied.

"Because you forgot?" the guard said, in a bid to challenge the reticent Ali.

"I remember like it was yesterday..."

"Come on, Ali, we're doomed to see each other every day, tell me what happened to you, so at least I can understand where you're coming from."

...

"Ali, *please*."

"My two children... their school was reduced to dust that very week... their mother lost in the rubble..."

"How?"

"Your *friendly* fire"

"...What happened to your children?"

"We travelled silently throughout the night. There were reports of helping hands waiting at a nearby border near the supposed tail end of the war. I knew it was our only chance of survival. I had no weapon to my name, nor the will to ever carry one. All I could carry were my brilliant son and daughter, one on each shoulder, and one night we went with my plan of escape. It was so difficult for us, my children, they were deeply traumatised, they witnessed things no children should see..."

"What did they see?" the guard responded, encouraging Ali to continue.

"Your merciless mercenaries, what they did to our land... Every night, for months, my poor children would break out into fits of hysteria, their crying voices piercing through the cold, ill-forgotten air of the night."

The guard remained silent, allowing Ali the space to gather his thoughts.

"Even if we remained hidden" continued Ali, "the sound of my crying children would alert nearby artillery and doom us all to a harrowing slaughter. I was determined to do whatever it takes to protect what was left of my family... I remembered an older wartime story my mother once told me. She was forced to feed me whiskey as a child, as the only method of helping me sleep in my terrorised state when we would stay awake to the sound of bombshells in neighbouring towns... Decades later, on the night of escape with my own children, I decided to give one sleeping tablet each to my son and daughter. It was all I had at the time. Within moments, they fell into a deep sleep, falling completely limp on each of my shoulders. I thought we could at least have a chance of escaping silently through the night...

After hours of walking, stumbling, and trekking through the night, we were so... thirsty... I was out of breath, I rested with my children in what I thought was a safe trench, deep into the countryside. We were so tired. I remember relaxing my eyes, just for a moment, until I was jolted awake from three gunshots fired from a distance. I could feel the wind of a bullet skim past my ear, penetrating softly into what sounded like soil. My face splattered with something warm.

Without thinking, I grabbed both of my children and ran across the trenches. I was so full of adrenaline... I ran with the might of an Olympic sprinter, my dear children still fast asleep, resting like feathers on my shoulders. I heard more gunshots fire as I locked in on a single hill, I ran downhill, fast, but soon tripped and fell. I threw both of my children onto the soft soil as they rolled down the hill and to a stop. I waited... all I heard was silence... I was unseen from any nearby forces. I stopped to take stock of the situation.

I gathered my two children nearby and held them both. I noticed one of them was limper than the other, my daughter, her face and neck was completely covered in blood... I-... don't know..."

"What happened, Ali?"

"I couldn't process what was happening. The pain was too much to handle. Without thinking, I started... digging, and digging... I remember the sand was wet with my tears."

"*Digging?*"

"The only consolation for me was at least to be able to ensure that my child had a dignified burial, and would rest peacefully in her own land. And then before I knew it, the sun was up, we made it until the morning... The sky was so bright. I marched, and marched, single mindedly, towards the border like an arrow. I don't remember how long, with my only child resting on my left shoulder... I saw faces in the distance. I collapsed... and... that's all... that's all I remember."

"I don't understand" replied the guard. "When I saw you, I remember you carrying your... dead... son, not your daughter."

"Yes... I- I can't say..."

"What, Ali?"

Ali looked down at the ground and sighed in grief, he covered his head in shame "in my sad, hopeless adrenaline-fuelled rage, in the cold, darkness of the night... I..."

"You did what, Ali?"

"I buried the wrong child... 3 feet deep into the soil... I buried the wrong child!" Ali drowned in anguish as he relived his nightmare. He could feel his will to live leave his body at that moment. He dropped his head to the floor, his fists and eyes painfully clenching, searching for some sense to his hopeless situation. A devout Christian man, true to his faith, screamed God's name with every last fibre of his being. "WHY?!" he asked the sky. "What did I do wrong? Why did you do this to me? My children? How can you let this happen? What am I to do with this pain? Please have mercy on me, my Lord, what am I to do with my pain? Please answer me! Answer me, NOW!" the echoes of his cries pierced like darts into the ears of the nearby men, shaking them into fear.

He turned to face the guard intensely and said "And you think this is why I won't accept your offer? You think this is why I refuse to sign away my soul and work for your puppeteers? For what your country did to my wife and children? No, my family are but three reasons, of a thousand more. For I know that for every story like mine, there are a thousand more that go undocumented, unaccounted for and unheard of. And if you have any decency left in you, you would grant my last wish to let me die in this cell. I failed my duty to my family. Burn all of my books, destroy my pretty words. My work means nothing anymore. My Lord has abandoned me, and I have abandoned my faith. I am done with this world. I am done with this life..."

The guard, unable to look Ali in the eye, "I'm sorry, Ali I.." he paused and gazed at the ground.

He left Ali in the prison cell that day.

CHAPTER

3

Time became a persistent fiend that day. The hours drudged painfully by... both infinite and merciless, Ali felt a renewed sense of bluntness. Losing his usual patience, he could no longer entertain the prospect of hope. A deep, menacing lethargy consumed him. With no pen, paper or reading material by his side, the panoramic emaciation of his mind lay bare. He knew perfectly well that he would never accept the offer, and that his death was inevitable. So with these considerations, he had nothing to fall back on but his own inner life. Realizing this and determined to live according to it, he settled down quietly into a deep contemplation.

He thought of his family and his life before the war. He thought about his wife, Salma, how she kept him company by his desk. How she helped him with his writing, how her elegant handwriting emanated seamlessly from the beauty of her gentle hands. He thought about his son, Michael, how he would cling to his mother's legs as she left early in the morning for work, and his daughter Elizabeth... sweet Elizabeth, wishing he could hold her tight and see her magnificent smile.

Ali thought, until thinking became difficult. Lost in his memories, he held the faces of his family alive on loop, constantly replaying in the weary recorder of his mind.

"One day I will be with you..." he whispered. "One day I will make it up to you..."

He sat silently, resting a solemn gaze on the dark stone wall in front of him.

Within moments, he heard a faint voice, echoing like a swirling vortex around the four walls of his cell.

"*Once upon a time...*" it said.

"What? Who was that?" Ali's heart raced. Startled, an adrenal rush dilated his pupils in an instant.

"There were three wise Elders who gathered around..."

"Who? What's going on?!" Ali looked around in a panic.

"They came together, to decide the fate of the human soul".

"The soul? Am I hearing voices?" Ali assumed he had reached the frontier of insanity, "I knew this would happen... all this time alone has driven me mad..."

The voice continued:

"Revered as the most sacred energy in existence, the Elders selected a place where the *soul* would remain pure. The first

Elder said, 'put it in the highest mountains!' and another replied 'no, these humans will crawl up like ants, take it and put it in a museum and turn it into a trophy'. The second Elder said, 'then put it in the deepest of seas!' and another replied 'no they make deep seacrafts, these people, they'll go down and find it again'. The third Elder said 'Then put it behind the furthest of planets!' and another replied 'no, they'll make spacecrafts, they'll create a space race out of it and then use the technology to even harm themselves!'"

Ali sat upright, paralysed with fear.

"The Elders could not decide the fate of the human soul… until, a mysterious voice spoke from the shadows:

'Place the soul in man himself. That is where he is least looking'."

The voice dissipated into silence. Unable to move, an impetuous breeze gushed past Ali, blowing from a tiny window above him. Accelerating, the wind encapsulated the cell like a tornado, elevating Ali's hair as if he were in a state of static shock.

"Who are you?!" He demanded, "What's happening?"

The wind ceased and a formidable voice sunk into the depths of Ali's right ear:

"I am the voice inside your head."

"Aah!" Ali screamed in terror.

A cold sweat percolated through his chest, his heart arythmic. "Is this it?" He thought. "Have I really gone mad? Will this be my shameful fate?... Possessed by a Jinn? No...there's no such thing", he attempted to reassure himself. "But then why did the voice sound so... *real*?"

Ali lay immobile, suspended between two worlds, neither here nor there.

In a state of trance, silence prevailed.

.....

"What was that story? Where have I heard that before?" he whispered to himself.

"Don't you *remember* your own work? Your soul must be very tired. Stay with my voice and your memory will begin to sharpen."

"I don't understand..." said Ali, disoriented.

"Think... and think harder. Remember to look at your life... closer... can you sense that there is something amiss from all this?"

"What is missing?".. Ali had no recollection. "What do you mean? I...I don't know", he said stammering. "Are you real? Show yourself at once!"

The darkness of the four walls, mimicking a black hole, engulfed Ali. Suddenly, from a glowing sunburst of radiant fire, a shadowy laser-focused figure ignited out of vapour, wielding a great wand that seemed to emanate a power from one realm to another. The figure confronted Ali with a piercing glare.

"Get away from me" cried Ali, "you wicked spirit! I refuse to believe what I am seeing; I've truly lost my mind!"

"There is nothing that can harm you now, Ali" beamed the figure, "*you*, who have overcome the grandest of battles."

"But how can I perceive you? How do I know you are real?"

"Many dimensions exist that are beyond your sensory and conceptual ability, they define reality also! Recognise that this prison cell is not a prison cell, but only how your mind perceives it" he explained, alighting the four walls of the cell while gesturing with his glowing hands, "the signature a bat can detail from this room, seeing it in ultrasound, or a fly with xray eyes - neither looks upon my reality as you or I do. It's *frightening*, isn't it? To realize you can be in an environment that is nothing like the reality you perceive.

Your perceptions are there for one reason: to help you survive in this ecosystem. Hence, my appearance..."

"Am I dreaming?"..Ali cradled his head in his hands, eyes closed he couldn't bear to look any longer.

"This is no dream Ali. I have been sent here to guide you"

"By whom, the Devil?" Ali scoffed sarcastically.

"Hmm... not *entirely*..." replied the being, now concerned at his own confrontational nature. "Come on, Ali, you can talk to me. Try it, ask me anything!"

Painfully squinting at the blinding figure, Ali shaded his eyes with his palms. Traumatised and delirious from inertia, he remained eager to challenge his mysterious mirage "Alright... tell me then, what's the meaning of life?"

"Your question is irrelevant to the answer you wish to gain. You see, the question is not to inquire about the meaning of life, but to ask, 'If life had a meaning, what would it be?' Only from this position may you succeed in the objective of the question, which is to find a meaning that you feel is certain for *yourself*."

Ali turned his head from the being. Confronted with a thought-provoking answer he said, "That sounds familiar..."

"You're going to feel that a lot from now."

"What does that mean? What do you want from me?"

"I am here to teach you, Ali."

"Teach me? About what?"

"Well, tell me....What have you learnt from the life you have lived?"

"Why should I tell you anything?!"

"You don't have to... you can spend more time in silence if you prefer."

"No, wait!... Don't go," Ali pleaded, "I can't stand to be alone any longer."

"How nice of you..." the being replied softly. "So then, tell me about your life."

"Why... what do you want to know?"

"Tell me how you *feel*, and I will reward you with the answer to that which you seek."

"I feel like I am dreaming."

"I see."

"So, are you *real*?"

"I am as real as you are, Ali".... "Is it normal for you to feel like you are dreaming?"

"Yes, I feel like my whole life has been a dream..."

"Why is that so?"

"I don't know... perhaps you could tell me?"

"Well, I *could* tell you," continued the being "but that would spoil all the fun."

"This is fun to you?!" said Ali indignantly. "What kind of person are you?"

"I already told you. I am the voice inside your head."

"How is this possible?"

"As I am speaking to you, know that I am but the innate intellectual quality already in your mind. I am here to teach you. Soon, you will come to remember me for guiding your survival through your lifetime."

"*You* guided *me*? Through my life?"

"Correct, and from the moment you decided to embark on the journey of truth, I gave you the power of language, as my words illuminated the path you wished to seek."

"Magician man, if you claim to know everything, then tell me: where is my darling wife?"

"From the beginning of time, Salma was inherent in the very dust of your bones. And the moment you dedicated your life to truth, Salma was with you. She will be with you until the end of your days. Since you decided to give yourself selflessly to serve others, Salma shone through you as a radiant angel beside you. No truthful man walks through life entirely alone."

"How can I find her? Will I ever see her again?"

"Oh, Ali... you are both destined to live your eternal lives together. Soon, you will realise that Salma has guarded you through your many lives. Intertwined, so have you guarded and protected her. You both deserve the highest ranking in each other's hearts. And since you have earned the invaluable inner peace of *certain* love, you will be bound to each other regardless of the oscillations of the outer world. You will find Salma again, waiting for you in the eternal truth intrinsic within you."

"Please, teach me then. Help me understand... help me to learn the... truth intrinsic within me," yielded Ali.

"I am at your service. Embrace your intellect and you will find your answers therein."

"How do I embrace my intellect?"

"Think for yourself, Ali. If something doesn't immediately ring true, if it doesn't touch your core, then reject the idea. The only way to know if something is true is to experience it for yourself. With an open mind, seek and listen to all the highest ideals. Consider the most enlightened thoughts, then choose your path by yourself, unique to yourself. This simple way of living can take many lives for men to learn, and not everybody is successful; they do not know what is true and not true, even for themselves."

"But how can I truly know if something is real and true? How can I ever be certain?"

"Know that anything that makes you weak physically, intellectually, or spiritually should be rejected as poison. If it is devoid of life, it cannot be true. Truth is strengthening, empowering, enlightening and invigorating. This is what even the greatest of men, like you, fail to find."

"This is so hard to comprehend. Why is it so difficult?"

"Fear is the culprit, but it is not your fault. It is part of human nature to be very much *afraid* of knowing oneself. For to know oneself carries a great responsibility."

"What responsibility? What is so frightening about knowing oneself?"

"Each person is born with a sacred power more valuable than anything they can find in the material world. Not everyone has the strength to hold this power. People who truly know themselves carry a particular aura and heavy magnetism, a charisma that can emancipate from imprisonment anyone with a last drop of life in their veins. The awakened man cannot be enslaved – that is the difficulty – and he cannot be imprisoned. And Earth is like a prison except for the awakened man; a solitary confinement."

"I feel that I no longer belong to this world..."

"That may be so. The awakened man is the greatest stranger in this world; he belongs to no one. No organisation constrains his path, no community, no society, no nation. But such is his fate - and that is you, o' Ali!"

"Me? An *awakened* man? What an ambiguous description... what does that even mean?"

"When you embodied my spirit, you wrote many great works that accelerated the understanding of your society. And equal it be that through logic, you carefully learned to traverse and conquer your interior world; the home of your soul."

"If it is true that I owe my realisation... or my *awakening,* to your wisdom, tell me, what is the ultimate answer that I should know?" Ali enquired, the gears of his curiosity slowly unwinding.

"How would you like to know the mystery of yourself? After all, what is the use for knowledge, without the knowledge of yourself? From the first day that I extended your space machines to the stars and the galaxies, I invite you to reach further; extend your reach to the stars beyond the ether of your mind."

"How can I understand the mystery of myself?"

"Know that I cannot tell you what you don't already know yourself. As you recount your ancient memories, so you shall remember the wisdom you so deserved through your life in the egoic hell realm of Earth. Through your experiences you shall know yourself."

"And I will hang onto your every word. Tell me the straight path I have so far travelled."

"You gained your highest ranks by first thinking of what you wanted to become. Soon, you learnt that you become the manifestation of your repetitive thoughts, what your mind was preoccupied with you personified. This is how a man attains his greatest desires on Earth."

"Yes, but it was my own desires that caused me so much pain."

"Correct, Ali, as the ancient Egyptian Hermes once said: *the punishment of desire is the agony of in fulfillment*. After many years you learnt that when you desired something so great, it consumed you, it became all that you could think about. And your mind-power was limited by the fog of obsession with craving for what you wanted."

"But how else am I supposed to make decisions, if I'm not guided by what I desire?"

"By making decisions from a place of peace. Peace is clarity, act from this place of peace and your external results will cause you to receive what you desire the most in return."

Ali pondered on the words of this enigmatic apparition, eager to fare well in the intellectual debate. "So then... what you're saying is, all I really desired... was peace?"

"Is this not what you wrote about in your stories? Was this not the essence of all your narratives; that a man is to gain everything he thought he ever desired, only to realise that he already had the greatest treasure all along? Your heroic protagonists were always thrown into the internal reality of themselves in the final chapters of your books."

"Yes but they were just stories... besides, I don't think I can gain that state of peace anymore. Nowadays I can't even think clearly. I'm too filled with shame... all locked up in this cell... it's hard not to feel as if I'm some worthless criminal."

"Think, Ali. To think clearly, first see yourself clearly... Your *real* self, not the false-identities that you and the other humans portray in this world. To feel peace is to recognise and be at peace with your real self."

"I don't even know what my *real* self is anymore..."

"Remember, the truth is empowering. For starters, view yourself in a positive light... The way you see yourself is related to how much you believe you can achieve what you put your mind to. How you view yourself is directly related to living a successful life. When you view yourself positively, you will start trusting your own thoughts. When you trust your own thoughts, the brightest ideas will start flowing through you - all you must do is pick and choose the ones that will serve you and take action. You may try, and fail, but this is the journey that each awakening soul must go through. Persistence is the key to the vehicle that is patience."

"But that is impossible for me. After all I have done... I don't see myself in the light that I so want to be seen. I failed my duty as a father. No more am I the worthy man I used to be."

"Ah, but the power is in your hands, Ali. 'You' are simply a narrative that you tell yourself! You are far from the validation, or lack thereof, that you receive and give to yourself. Detach your identity from this and never compromise who you are."

"How do I know when I truly *know* myself? I mean, what are the signs?"

"Once you begin to know yourself, you start to know what to say and what to do without much thinking. You stop playing a character in the social theatre because when you become aligned with yourself, the world aligns with you.

Understanding this knowledge becomes your power. You already know this, Ali, your memory is just faded. Really, you used this knowledge wisely to write the beautiful works you so desired."

"Well, I suppose I remember when... my mind was clear, I could feel my intuition. It was as if a feeling was in my body guiding me to express what I felt. My instincts told me what to do, what to say, how to act... and that was the cause of gracefulness... But were those really my thoughts? Was I just a puppet; a passive witness, trapped in a destiny outside of my control?"

"Know this Ali, 'You' are a non-local awareness, independent of space or time. You are a consciousness that collapses the wave function of the material realm. Think about where your thoughts come from. You observe that your thoughts affect your actions, but if you want to find the origin of your thoughts, you must decipher the sensations in your body. First comes feeling, then comes thought."

Ali took a moment to absorb the dense packet of wisdom the glowing figure had thrown at him, before replying, "So then, what does that make me? A slave to my bodily feelings?"

"On the one hand you are a free consciousness, and on the other hand you are a biological robot."

"What does that mean?"

"For you, it meant that you managed to comprehend that your emotions didn't need to define you. You realised that emotions are there to be observed, acknowledged, their wisdom utilised, and transcended."

"I *transcended* my emotions?"

"Your memory is clearing, Ali! Now, relax, think... as you traversed the tests of the years, you sharpened your mind with the blade of your intellect. This is how you finally began to live consciously, not by accident. This is the starting point of the straight path to peace."

"And what does it mean, to live consciously?"

"You tell me! How would you like to be? Weak and doubtful, or strong and powerful?"

"I want to be strong powerful, of course! I want to be high and mighty to bring justice to this painful world."

"So ask yourself: What are you hanging onto that's stopping you from feeling powerful? Are there any conditions you have placed on yourself that prohibit you from achieving this state of empowerment?"

"Conditions... yes I mean, I can't just feel powerful all the time. There are various conditions, a few come to mind...

that's just normal though, no?"

"Do you want to be normal, Ali?"

"...No."

"That's what I thought. Which is why you need to let go of the conditions you place on yourself to get into an empowered state. Do you understand now?"

"Help me understand."

"Your ideals and judgements come from an illusory image of yourself that indirectly stifle your ability to serve the greatest good. Understand now, that you must remove the conditions you place upon yourself to feel the power that lays dormant in your spirit."

"Ah... so you're saying that I need to give myself permission to be empowered, to feel great, *no matter what*?"

"Yes, or in other words, if you want power, you need to first believe that you truly deserve it. Now tell me, what else do you remember?"

Ali felt challenged by the optimistic inquisition from his intellectual companion. He took his time to answer mindfully, sensing an upcoming realisation that had been brewing in his mind. A realisation that gave him the consolation he had been craving. "I remember!" he cried "I remember that good things always *happened* when I *felt* good inside. That is, it's as if... when the sensations in my body felt good, I created a positive force field which attracted further good experiences into my life. I wasn't sure if I was being delusional, but somewhere deep down I knew that negative thoughts and feelings were nothing but a lie; a human survival mechanism that serves no purpose in man's fulfilment"..."But really, what difference can I really make to the world, when I am only one person?"

"You may be a singular man, yes, but every man is a node in a larger network of people. If we take that each person interacts with say, 10 people per week, and each singular encounter then has the ability to touch a further 10 people. This means, when you influence 1 person, you indirectly influence 10 others without even knowing it."

"So... you mean that one person indirectly influences 100 people per week, if everyone interacts with 10 people a week?"

"Yes, and then, after 52 weeks, you would have indirectly influenced the lives of thousands, and possibly hundreds of thousands in one lifetime, just through the simple act of conversation. Call it the butterfly effect if you will, or simple mathematics. This is an innate power that men are so inclined to forget."

"Why?"

"Because they lack the perception."

"I see... Well, how did I fare in my interaction with others? Did I make an impact?"

"You fared well, old man, you should be proud!"

"Really... but how?" asked Ali, as he scratched his head urging himself to remember.

"You made it your principle to uplift every person you interacted with; making them feel good about themselves. With the satisfaction you gained from your work and your family, you began to feel so *good* about yourself that it infused onto others... you recognised that your best self is your confident self. And in essence, confidence equates to relaxation. Letting your guard down around others was your habitual state, this was of great value to whomever crossed your path. Were you not confident, playful and carefree when you were a child, playing in the Garden?"

"...Yes, when I was a child... I was always held in the warm, embracing love of nature... of my caring mother and father. I had no idea of what was bad."

"But when you went through your many Earthly challenges, you became stern, rigid, judging... that was, until you learnt to integrate your heart and soul into your world mission."

"I did *what*? How did I do that?"

"You integrated your heart and soul by embodying the ideal character."

"The ideal character? What's that..? Where are you going with this?"

Determined to take Ali through an illuminating journey to recall his thoughts, the figure continued, "Your ideal character emerged when you carried both the strength of a man and the playfulness of a child... this combination allowed your core confidence, your artistic genius, to seep out from your being."

"The strength of a man and the playfulness of a child... I wrote about this once... those magical moments; it's as if something takes over me, a certain power... inspirational, light and creative... But it never lasts, why?"

"Because while people have fleeting moments of joy, life's responsibilities catch up, as do people's personalities."

"What's wrong with people's personalities?"

"Personalities are a product of the past; a past that carries conflict, a past that holds disappointment, of blunt obligations. It is this ugliness, the harsh reality of life; society's strive for survival, a collective and subtle trauma, that manifests itself in the character of mankind. And this ugliness that people sense in themselves is not theirs to behold, despite its real physical condition and the monotonous experiences that plague their days. When people sense this, consciously or not, they feel a great discontentment within themselves, they begin to carry a certain dead weight."

"A dead weight?"

"People live with the heaviness of the inability to accept all the disparate parts of themselves. They feel imperfect, as if they must conceal their unsavoury sides, and only showcase a select, more appealing fragment of their persona. But when a man learns to accept even the most undesirable segments of himself, he becomes free from the pendulum of the meteoric ups and the oceanic lows that life concocts. He regains an innate strength, one that overflows from the beautiful fountain of his soul... Just as you did, Ali."

"I did? How?"

"When you freed your mind from psychological inefficiencies, judgement, resistances, limitations and paradoxes, you created a space for my wisdom to pour into you. I, the voice in your head, the light of your inspiration, became more embodied in your potential, until you merged with my essence and became the light of your own world."

"I see... well, if that indeed is the case, I am indebted to you, intellect man. I see now that my ability was knowledge that emanated from your divine light."

"And it was through this light that you conquered the arts, and wrote works that refined the coarse perimeters of your society. Your words sharpened the swords of truth, sheathed in every man's conscience!"

"So it was you, all this time, working through me? ...Is this the same for everyone?"

"Know this Ali"... the magical being continued, gesturing his wand and manifesting a holographic illustration of his teachings:

"*Every book that has ever been written has been written by the same author.* Every building that has ever been built has been built by the same engineer. The creations happened because the conscious mind of the writer and the engineer did not present any negative subconscious programming. So that which was within, was able to explode into the moment and behind the thoughts of the creator, was an essential voice '*yes I can, yes I can*'".

"All of the Sages and Prophets of old...", began Ali, with a newfound expression of wonder, "they always emphasised the same rhetoric. The great Zoroaster himself said: '*Do not pray to me. Go right to the source. The source is in you, and that's what will set you free'*... tell me, what does this really mean?"

"It means that you must learn to dispel the thoughts protruding from the outside, and tune in to the thoughts emitting from the inside. This is what you do in meditation. The thoughts that came from the outside made you fearful, miserable... When you figured this out, you realised that you are the light of this world."

"Now I see that for many years, what I consciously desired was counteracted by my subconscious mind, which in itself held opposite thoughts, past traumas and insecurities."

"Correct, Ali. And so you succeeded to nurture your subconscious mind, through deep contemplation I guided you to prune your inner sanctuary and plant great seeds of wisdom. I saw you transform into a completely more evolved person, but it was difficult, as you struggled to understand the mechanics of how to do this over time."

"Then appease my confusions so I no longer fall from grace. How do I clean up my subconscious mind?"

"Take no thought. Go into emptiness. And allow the universal law of physics to explode within you; the creative power that comes from nothingness/emptiness," instructed the mystical being, closing his eyes with a silent smile. "It is only through silence, wakeful devoted silence... silence surrendered to the ultimate truth of pure consciousness, that enables the accumulation of spiritual energy to a point where all of the wonderful things of the Universe will explode into activity. You are a veteran of this, Ali. You, who took yourself out of the authority of creation, and put yourself into the authority of the creator."

"Is that true?" asked Ali.

"In contemplating indiscriminately on teachings from all subjects, you unearthed the sacred knowledge of alchemy; of turning lead into gold, of overcoming crude matter through spiritual truths. As such, through your long, arduous and conscious journey, you looked for ways to turn disappointing situations and setbacks into opportunities, to learn, grow, and become a better person. For when you truly embraced your intellect, you were able to shift your perspective to recognise the benefits of even the harshest of days. It was in this approach that you were able to transcend the darkness, which is your doubt; and became guided by your own light, which is your essence."

"All this talk of my essence... it seems... optimistic, mystical, secretive..."

"It was this very optimistic and mystical undertaking that made you *believe* life was working for your highest good. You stopped complaining about your adversities and grew to enjoy working toward a grander vision. This provided with you the mental resilience to accept the ups and downs."

"All I wanted was to provide a beautiful life for my family. I was grateful for the responsibility. Giving up never crossed my mind. But now I have no family... and without my children, my dear Salma, I will never be the man I once was."

"Is that so, Ali?"

"I owe everything to my family. My children were my mission, and it was my wife who gave me the clarity of mind, the mental resilience of which you speak. Salma was my one true source of peace, and it is something no book or teaching could give me. My soul belongs to her."

"You can get through this, Ali. Knowledge can set you free."

"Ah, but Magi man," Ali requited, a semblance of frustration in his tone, "if you really were all-knowledgeable, you would know that your intellectualism is a common cover-up for the fear of direct experience. You have not dived into love as you are afraid of losing yourself. Your wanting to know everything makes you afraid of the unknown. By your knowledge alone, you will not dive into unseen horizons and embrace the highest wisdom only found in true love."

"All the truths are already within you, Ali."

"And 'all truths are but half-truths', as your favourite Hermes once said. You claim to be all-knowing, but I know a meaning that you can not understand. You claim to be the master of thought, but you forget that it is the heart that nourishes the mind."

"You are beginning to sound like the Ali I know…"

"What do you mean?"

The figure's glowing gaze locked eyes with Ali "*You are too great for my logic gate,*" he declared with a half-pleased smile, "*alas, there are things the heart knows that the mind alone cannot understand*" he concluded, beginning to fade away, revealing more of the stone wall behind him.

"Where are you going?" said Ali "Wait… what am I to do here?"

"Let go, Ali" the being's voice receding.

"Tell me then, please, before you go, how do I let go?"

"*Letting go is just breathing without thinking…*"

The fading figure closed his eyes, gently dissolving back into the nothingness from which he came.

Ali was left staring into the opaque void of the night. He gazed down towards the ground, his heart racing, trying to make sense of what just happened. A million thoughts raced through his mind. He tried to calm himself with deep breaths as a subtle euphoria filled his veins. He remained quiet for a while, as the silence of the night time helped him collect his thoughts.

"The heart knows... what the mind can't understand... what does that mean?" he thought to himself. "My thoughts have made me weak? What did he mean by that? What did I mean by that? And *where have I heard that before*?"

Ali thought about the cryptic declamation of the mysterious figure. "Align with yourself and the world will align with you..." he remembered. Ali felt defensive, insecure; intellectually violated, and yet strangely inspired. After all, it was the sort of intellectual ricochet he'd been craving, one that he hadn't had the pleasure of experiencing for a while.

He continued staring intensely at the stone wall and pondered on the exchange "If the thoughts from the outside have made me weak... what is it that makes me strong?" Ali thought. He consolidated his new-found curiosity with a burning question: "'draw thoughts from the inside', he said... but where is inside?... meditation... he said *meditation*... right?"

Ali frantically searched the cell with his eyes, desperately seeking some inanimate comfort, but it was barren. A burning reminder of his hopeless captivity. He looked down at his wrists, blistered and chained in heavy metal shackles. "Well... there's nothing else I can do here."

Ali humbly asked for one more piece of guidance:

"Voice in my head, if you're still there, teach me how to let go of thoughts from the outside. Tell me how to realise my own essence and find my truth. Guide me, if you will. Teach me, *how do I draw from within?*"

Ali sat up straight and took three, long, deep breaths. Inhaling the cold air, he felt a chilly breeze hit his face, goosebumps spreading across his arms as a rejuvenating shiver travelled up his spine.

He closed his eyes and waited, silently. Until, the voice spoke back.

In an intimate whisper, the voice appeared to emanate from Ali's own mind, grazing the surroundings of the cell, surrounding him in an auditory ripple:

"To understand the essence in which the flame is filled, one must learn to make the fire still.

Your truth is a sacred flame, blazing in the darkness of your subconscious mind.

Past creates the darkness, future is the womb, awareness is your present;

A gift from above, with patience, in your journey through time you shall find.

Every time you conceive a thought, focusing on breath is your solution.

For once in your life, focus your awareness, on your awareness.

There lies your evolution.

Turn your attention around back onto itself.

Become aware of the fact that you are aware.

Do not focus on the thought of awareness,

focus on awareness itself.

Become close to the light of your consciousness,

become one, with the consciousness.

You have become so engrossed in the physical world,

that you have distanced yourself from the very awareness that colours your world.

In turning to that awareness, and focusing on where that awareness is coming from, ask yourself:

Where is my awareness?

Where is my awareness located?

In your head? Your heart?

Or your gut?

Feel about it, don't think about it.

Sit feelingly, not thinkingly.

Focus on the fact that you are focused.

While you are looking for your awareness, thoughts will arise, and that is okay.

Dip into the experience of having a thought, not the thought itself.

The experience is simply 'I am'.

Thoughts exist because you make thoughts possible.

When thoughts come, observe, disengage, and return to your breath.

Forgive yourself for having thoughts, again, and again.

Allow the thoughts to arise, but know they are far from yourself.

Over time, awareness itself will become your sense of self,

This is how you return to your essence.

Return to your observing self.

Rest here, consolidate your thoughts.

Allow them to reach their conclusion.

There is nothing for you to do.

There is nobody you need to be,

There is nothing you need to say.

Sit back and watch nature work for you.

The more you focus on the 'I';

of becoming aware of being aware,

the more the mind goes inward.

Until, you merge back with the source that is your true self.

To reach peace of mind is to know oneself.

To know clearly, just for a moment,

Is to indulge in clarity of purpose.

Remind yourself of yourself throughout the day, throughout the night.

Train this muscle,

until you gain the strength to tear this dream apart.

To hear your essence speak,

is your reminder,

of what you came here to do."

Ali followed these words as he slowly fell into a deep, focusing trance. His thoughts turned into distant echoes as he sat still, listening, focusing on the silence.

The hours passed like a dream; the sunlight matured into a mellow glow. Ali listened ardently to the gentle rainfall outside. He could taste the earthy smell displaced from the wet, nourished soil. He remembered reading about the nostalgic scent in Greek mythology.

"Petrichor" he thought, "the fluid that flows in the veins of the Gods. How beautiful."

Resting in deep contemplation, Ali observed his mind thoroughly and honestly, shining light on all its tendencies. He saw memories charged with fear, anger, judgment, guilt, and shame. Ali felt a little afraid even of his own mind, but viewed this as a blessing. It was indicative of his evolving self.

He reflected, whilst his reflection restored a level of awakening and transformation in his heart and mind. A new source of internal splendour.

Ali rested in this awareness as his meditation captured him, carrying him safely into a deep sleep through the night.

CHAPTER

4

But all good things must come to an end, and Ali's mental oasis was no exception. For just as his thirst for peace was satiated, he returned to a world that tried it's best to absorb the dry reality of his fortified cell. Ali awoke that morning to the melodious song of birds singing in the distance, a sound he savoured as a daily source of comfort for his melting mind. His daydream was soon interrupted as he flinched at the sudden rustling of keys; the guard clamoring to unlock his prison cell. The guard arrived later than usual. Perhaps to give Ali the sanctity to rouse of his own accord.

As he walked into the cell, he balanced an exotic platter of chopped fruits and breakfast tea in one hand, and clasped an old book in the other. The guard knelt carefully and placed the tray on the floor. Ali, almost oblivious to the grand gesture in front of him, looked at the tray with uneasy suspicion. "You're upgrading me to 3 stars?", he said mockingly.

He saw the guard postured upright, flicking eagerly through the book, his fingers hovering over paragraphs as if to find a specific text. "Aha!" he said, "this is the page". He blew away the residual dust that was embedded between the pages.

"I want you to tell me the meaning of this passage" the guard said, as he held his arms stretched out.

Ali looked at him, surprised.

The guard kept his eyes fixed on the open page, "are you ready?", he said, shaking the book in front of Ali's face.

But before Ali could reply, the guard inhaled deeply and started to narrate: "I am a breath, and I am everyone. Your voice is my voice, your word is my word. Your image is my image. Your conversation is my conversation" he paused, turning over the dusty page.

Ali listened, curious.

"You, who have looked for me, have found me; have found yourself in your own self," the guard continued, "Your being aware of this means grasping the truth. My name is your name. My spirit is your spirit. My eye is your eye. I look at the realms through you, I think through you, I observe through you, I evolve through you" he recited proudly, intermittently lowering the book to check Ali's attentiveness. Seeing that his eyes were closed, he exclaimed, "Are you listening?"

"Hmm? Yes, your voice is very soothing. Please, carry on"

The guard turned once more to the page, wincing in concentration as he read "Find me neither in thought nor in material... When I am a thought, I am the entire skies. When I am a substance, I am all the souls...

I am the riverbed of the river flowing tranquilly. I am the foam of the stream flowing wildly. I am the mirror of a thinking whole. I am the one who adds learning to the learning of the cosmos. Climates are me, heavens are me, Suns are me, folding mountains are me..." he paused, letting out another deep breath, preparing to dictate the next lines carefully and intensely:

"WHO AM I?

I AM A BEAUTIFUL HABIT.

UGLINESS ARE MY CRUST.

BEAUTIES ARE MY DIVINE LIGHT.

IF YOU LOOK FOR ME, I AM YOU...."

He slammed the old book shut as the dust permeated the air like silken vapor, escaping pages that had been frozen in time. He looked expectantly at Ali.

Amused, Ali addressed him casually, "The last bit sounded better in my head."

"Why do all of your books end with this same last chapter?" the guard asked Ali.

"To be honest I don't know, the English translation doesn't make much sense. Do you speak Arabic?"

"Come on, Ali..." the guard said, almost pleading. "I'm being serious, I want to know the meaning of your words."

"But why?" Ali was tired and perplexed.

"Ali... I will get reprimanded if I am caught talking to you, but..." The guard knelt closer to Ali and continued in a low whisper. "Look, I couldn't understand why you were the only prisoner allotted to one guard, watched over like a dignitary... and why was it YOU who received a proposition from the Ministry, something that evades even our most experienced and loyal comrades? You know it's no small feat to be selected to join the *intelligence* agency, right?"

"So, what's your point?"

"The whole world knows of your work, Ali. But very few know you are here" the guard said, looking carefully over his shoulders to check for nearby listeners, "When you were captured, the Ministry reported you as dead. For some time, masses across continents *mourned* your death. Unbeknown to you, crowds gathered in every major city, chanting 'long live prophet Ali'. Now, I want to know what the truth is at the heart of your work, I want to understand the meaning of your words as you seem to be some sort of great sage."

Ali scoffed and turned his head towards the high window above him. "I am not a prophet" he rebuffed, "nor a sage", he said, reaching for his tea, before lowering the glass back down again in disappointment, "this tea is cold."

"Who are you, Ali?"

Ali turned to look the guard in the eye and hesitated before responding, "Well... I was a school teacher, and sometimes I wrote stories."

The guard mulled over Ali's words.. "So why did you write the same passage in every one of your books?"

"Okay, look... young man... if you must know, I haven't told this to anyone before. The true meaning is a great secret..."

"A *secret*?"

"Yes, and well, look, I can't just tell *anyone*..."

"Well you can tell me!"

"Hmm..." Ali mused, stroking his beard "are you sure I can trust you to keep it to yourself?"

"Yes, of course!"

"I need your utmost assurance that you will keep this knowledge strictly between me and you and whatever happens, do not run to the *intelligence* agencies with this powerful information."

"Yes, yes, I mean no, I won't... you have my word!"

"Promise?"

"I promise."

"On your life?"

"On my life!

"Alright, young man... You want to know who spoke those words?"

"Who?"

"They call him... the great programmer."

"The great... *programmer*..."

"Yes, the great programmer... from the central system."

"The central... *system*..."

"Yes, the central system... of an ancient ordinance from the times beyond time! He was the initial one, the divine emissary who built the secret code."

"The secret code... what secret code?"

Ali gestured his hand for the guard to come closer, and whispered "...Come here and I'll tell you. It's a truth so secret, I have to make sure no one can hear."

"Tell me." the guard said eagerly.

"There is no easy way to say this." Ali continued, enjoying his game of suspense.

"What?"

"We're living"...

"..."

"...in a *simulation*."

The guard's eyes widened in anticipation "...*really*?"

Unable to maintain the charade any longer, Ali erupted into laughter. Seemingly pleased with himself. Humiliated by a *prisoner*, the guard stormed angrily towards the door without looking back. Unable to contain his spontaneous burst of joviality, Ali's laughter reverberated down the stoney corridor. "What's wrong? You leave me alone..." he cried after him "then deny me the chance to make a little joke?!"

Turning hot on his heels "That was your second strike" the guard snapped back, "I'm giving you one last chance. You're lucky we're still keeping you here. I'll be back tomorrow but this time there won't be any more papers. I know how much you love to read and write, but now you'll pay for your attitude with solitude" he said condescendingly, slamming the metal door shut behind him.

"Lucky?.. Ali recoiled. "Next time you ask me to sell my soul, try to at least make me a decent cup of tea!"

CHAPTER

5

A nother day, the same old night. Our abandoned pacifist, with boredom, did he fight. Ali perpetually encountered sadness, feeling becalmed in the almighty ocean of time. Ali's longing for stimulus remained, his weary mind, a frayed archive of a lifetime now overplayed, books concluded and records faded. He searched pedantically, inspecting each detail. Double-checking for things he may have missed; restoring memories he may have forgotten, meanings yet to be uncovered, perspectives yet to be found. Intense dormancy acquainted Ali with the realisation that newness itself was a blessing he once took for granted. The freedom to walk the streets of his old home, to spark a conversation, to think of something fresh, were all an ever-distant delicacy. Jaded in his quest for novelty and purpose, Ali sat ruminating, shining light on his thoughts and feelings in an audacious attempt to find something new.

"A prophet..." he recalled, "is that really how I sound?"

Ali deliberated on this for a while. He felt ashamed at the thought of being idolised - as if his integrity were balancing on a string. "This world has gone mad..." he sighed "if only they could see me now..."

This unthinkable notion had left a loathsome taste on his conscience. Adamant to revisit a numbed, meditative escape, he settled down quietly. He closed his eyes and centred on his thoughts, this time observing rather than residing in them, reminiscing on the advice from his mysterious friend:

"Feel about it, don't think about it.

Sit feelingly, not thinkingly.

Focus on the fact that you are focused."

The hours coalesced into one as Ali floated in a realm of devotion. For now, in the passing river of time, a silent mind and a resting heart were all he could ever hope for. As the daylight lay to rest, his thoughts mellowed with the sunset, sinking deep below the horizon. He remained serenely focused as the dark of night encompassed. It wasn't long until focusing became easier than thinking. In fact, *focus* soon became his close friend, one who knew how to soothe him, and to hold him, as his body began to wane. Focus grew into his night watch, a loyal soldier, primed to guard the king against the adversary of thought.

Ali let go of all effort. The light of his awareness dispersing the invading influences of the outside, as he fell through the needle's eye of his mind; an exclusive portal to inspiration that only patience can find. Ali sat deeply still, mentally miming the ancient orchestra of silence, the sacred melody of the subconscious. He could hear the gentle wind breathing through the leaves outdoors, he could hear his heartbeat gently in his chest. In silence he dined, as the hours passed by, until swiftly, a new memory was aroused; a voice whispering in his mind, an excerpt from a reflection once left behind:

"If thoughts were a forest, focus would be a flower.

A seed so minute, unnoticeable, but subtle in its power."

The voice caressed the four corners of the walls. Ali opened his eyes, thinking his previous acquaintance had come back to visit, but instead he saw a newly majestic figure, framed in the backdrop of the moonlight.

The figure resembled the look of the previous being, but as his hypnotic eyes gazed closer, endearingly toward him, Ali realised this was someone he had never met before. The being held one arm outstretched as if to offer a helping hand, a semblance of mercy; a showcase of love. This comforted Ali, his initial shock grounded by the warming serenity seeming to exude from the friendly being. Ali watched in awe, waiting to hear the rest of the oration from this new raconteur:

*"Rising from the soil, a delicate stem
withstanding nature's test,*

Growing in strength, the flower blooms until standing feels like rest.

Relaxing in her glory, not long before she withers away,

The flower lives for the effortless grace of those colourful days.

So is your focus, an idea planted from above, a flower yet to be bloomed,

Nourished by your light, purpose is its food.

Raise your focus as a mother raises her young with a smile,

Until the day comes, when the mother grows tired,

And she may rest in the arms,

Of her strong, old child."

Ali felt pleased with these words "I didn't know they made an English version of that verse" he said.

"Of course, Ali, your work is coloured by many cultures, enjoyed in all its shades and hues."

"Who are you?" enquired Ali.

"*I am the voice in your heart.*"

"My *heart*?... But how do I hear you?"

"When the mind is silent for long enough, it is your heart that speaks."

"Are you a figment of my mind's imagination?"

"I am more than your mind alone can imagine, as your mind is an empty space for your heart."

"So does that make you... my conscience?"

"I fuel your conscience, Ali. And I am here to remind you that which you need to know"

"Ugh. You're here to remind me that I've lost my mind..." he said, starting to feel somewhat dejected... "I don't even have the strength to question this anymore... What do I need to know about?" he asked wearily... "Love?"

"I am here to remove the separation between that which you know as *you*, and that which is your true nature, which is love."

Ali wrestled his mind for a good while, eager to solve this cryptic conundrum from his friendly foe. "What you're saying is that my mind is split, and the heart is the one who can fill the gaps, with love, to make me become whole?"

"At the dawn of existence, everything was whole in the first instance. Only afterwards did the Universe separate into many pieces and formed you and all of the world's contradictions out of its elements. You, who are made in this image, feel this separation deep within your being. It is this separation that is the cause of the chaos in this world. Mankind is walking around feeling he is missing something, and men spend their lives searching, hoping that one day they will reach some reward to fill this hole in their core. So I came here to give *you* that missing, *something*."

Ali took his time to reflect on these words, savouring his refreshed teachings, allowing them to settle in his cognition. Mindful of this unique opportunity and welcomed insight, he paused for a moment before asking his burning, but simple question "Tell me then, what *is* love?"

"Love is a great vibration that cannot be fitted into petty feelings."

"Vibration?" he asked.

"Feelings are your physical desires. They are not love. Love is such a vibration whos' frequency waves envelope the entire Universe. The same waves that enveloped you, as you wandered in your Garden with your family. The same love that reflected the creator's beauty within you. Thus, your life on Earth arose with your eloquence to beauty. And as

Salma's love ran through you, you lived a life full of this beauty, and it is exactly this beauty that drove your evolution."

"I see... Well, have I grown well? Did I love *genuinely*?"

"When you were a young soul, thrown into the Earth realm, your mind was scattered; overwhelmed with the world of forms. And whilst you progressed elegantly over the years, advancing in your internal search for your treasure, you learned to give love, but not genuinely at first. When your love was not genuine, your ideas formed feelings that were temporary as they were restricted by your animal mind."

"What is the difference between animal love and genuine love?" Ali asked, curious to learn more.

"When love is genuine, you give without expectation of reciprocity. Genuine love requires one to purify their intentions. Eventually, over many years, you became integrated with your true nature by first understanding your animal mind... its tendencies, and trickeries, which you overcame through the enduring power in your heart. Only then, were you able to give genuine love without the expectation of reciprocity. In your genuine love for your family, marvellous vibrations arose currents from within you, melting in all beatitude. As you transcended beyond your limits of thought and creation, you wrote a thousand lifetimes of works in one life."

Ali thought for a moment, wondering if the mysterious teachings rang true to him. "When I think about my dear Salma" he said "I feel a tranquil wave washing over me... With this feeling, all of my stories and poems would write themselves... it's as if I just know what to do, and say."

"Correct. And these beautiful currents will always guide you, on the condition you don't place any obstacle in their way. This is how, in your forgotten life, you were able to find your genuine happiness. You discovered that true love means giving from your essence."

"For decades I proliferated in my writings, I wished that these beautiful feelings may shine in the hearts of all those from every corner of the world. Remind me... in your words - or my heart's words - what does it mean to give from my essence?" inquired Ali.

"To give from your essence is to recognize and express your true nature. This is the greatest service one can render humanity. This is your purpose, Ali, and it is the path I am here to guide you to follow."

"My purpose? ... I have no purpose; I am condemned to this prison cell. My only option is to work for the Devil or die here. I will spend the rest of my life here, cold, hungry and alone."

"And is this why you are acting out of character?"

"Out of character? How so?"

"I saw how you dismissed that poor prison guard. There was no love in your actions, why, Ali?"

"Why should I respond to the queries of a man who locked these chains to my hands, who serves the institution that destroyed my family?"

"But he is not the man who wrote the order of the regime. Like you, he is simply caught in the crossfire. More so, his willingness to learn of the healing wisdom you propagate was a purposeful opportunity to fight for what you believe in."

"A purposeful opportunity... there is no purpose left in this world, where the pure are considered insane and the impure are honoured as wise..."

"...Where the madman is believed as brave, and the wicked esteemed as good?"

"So you agree?"

"Impartiality is in my nature, Ali. I choose not to agree nor to disagree."

"Then what do you think? If you were me, how would you make sense of my hopeless situation?"

"Well, I am your *heart*, so it is easy for me to say..."

"To say what?"

"That I would forgive, of course!"

"Just like that? Forgive *them*? How could you be so weak, to make such a passive decision?"

"For me, forgiving is a strong and wise decision, one that is necessary to create the world I envision."

"And I am wise enough to know that everything has its own time and place... and this is not the time or the place for forgiveness. You see, that's the problem with following your *heart*, before you know it, you find yourself on a path ready-made for a fool."

"It doesn't hurt to try a different path, occasionally. You should try being a fool."

"I don't understand... why?"

"All the best people are foolish in their own unique ways. Your lofty ideals shouldn't discriminate against those who are a free spirit. You see, the spirit just wants to play, and when the spirit plays, deep purpose is fulfilled."

"But you can't just play. In real life, you must think logically, carefully, and plan what you're going to do."

"Well, not all the time, Ali."

"Then help me understand... do you have an example?"

"Nikola Tesla perhaps! The great inventor, the foreseer of a world yet to be known. He loved only two things: his pigeon and his creations. He foresaw a future where man would be able to communicate at any distance with a device that fit in the vest of his pocket."

"But what do you mean? Nikola Tesla was an intellectual; a scientist."

"And what was the source of this genius?"

"Let me guess... his heart?"

The being of Love began to quote the famous phrase, his words echoing with the glowing gestures of his hands:

"My brain is only a receiver, in the Universe there is a core from which we obtain knowledge, strength and inspiration. I have not penetrated into the secrets of this core, but I know that it exists." – Nikola Tesla

When he finished, he narrowed his attention back to Ali and asked, "What do you think he meant by this?"

"The mysterious source of inspiration"... "many great artists have spoken of this. And I see you're trying to take the credit."

"And where do you think we'd be without the electric motor, or wireless communication? Yet, Nikola died without a dime to his name. A wonderful fool with nothing to prove. Do you think that intellect alone can carry a man to this vision?"

"Mr. Lover" said Ali with a patronising lilt, "I feel that I already know these things... I have read and conceived this for a long time now. But it's almost as if I must remind myself every day. In a repeated nature, I constantly rise and fall from grace. Why is it so difficult to embody a truth, if you already know it to be true in your mind?"

"Your mind is quick to grasp the surface of a truth, but your body needs time to digest the deeper emotional gist of it. A body is like a brain that carries the memories of feelings, rather than images. Open up to your heart with patience and discipline, slowly you will reveal and deal with the feelings that distance you from the deep peace and clarity you wish to seek."

"All this talk of peace and clarity... What's the point? I'm stuck here in this cell."

"First peace, then clarity of purpose, and then you can make the right decision. Do not let your anger waste the opportunity that knocks at your door."

"The opportunity to work for *them*? My mind won't even permit me to consider such an act."

"Then don't try... let go. Remember, your mind is a tool to draw yourself out from your heart."

"My heart is saying that I can never forgive that evil regime for what they did to my family, to my people."

"*I am* your heart, Ali, and I am telling you that if you fail to forgive, you are of no use to anyone. Besides..." he continued, a little flustered "think about it, you may have an opportunity to sabotage their plans from the inside. Isn't that what you were thinking? To at least have some chance of a new life; one with purpose, possibilities and reward?"

"That was just a crazy idea I had."

"A crazily *good* idea! What's stopping you from accepting such a heroic path?"

"As much as my heart wants to believe, you cannot simply enter the belly of a monster and tear it apart from the inside, not before it devours you first. Do you not know how these institutions work?"

"You can do it, Ali."

"But, it just doesn't feel right... I'm sorry, my gut tells me it's just not possible."

"Don't you think you have the ability to lead a team if you went there, with *compassion* and *empathy*? Humans are social animals after all, with your charisma and articulation, you could offer the kind of leadership to inspire an army of strong comrades to follow."

"You expect too much of me. Besides, I already told you, I have lost the source of inspiration that once fuelled my influence. I am a maverick who has fallen from grace; I am no longer fit for such accolades."

"Then answer me this....If you were walking through a forest and saw a tree, limp and dying, what would you think of that tree?"

"Are you digressing? What's this got to do with anything?"

"Answer me, please. What would you do? Would you regard a dying tree as a bad tree?"

"No... a tree is just a tree, it responds to its environment, the sun, water, the nourishment it gets from the soil."

"So it's not the tree's fault that it is dying?"

"No."

"Well I'm afraid we have a predicament here, Ali."

"Why?"

"Because you give the trees more patience and understanding than yourself. You, who have faced much greater hardships and responsibility, should surely be held in equal standing."

"What's your point?"

"I am saying, the reason you find it difficult to sign those papers is not because you cannot forgive the regime of that poor prison guard... really, you cannot bring yourself to move on because you refuse to forgive *yourself*. After all this time, you still haven't forgiven yourself for the tragic mistake you made that one, unfortunate night."

Ali winced and covered his face with his hands as he recounted that heinous memory. "How can I?!" he yelled "What I did was unspeakable, catastrophically clumsy, I lost my family because of my negligence, my weakness, my inability to act responsibly when my poor children needed me the most!"

"But Ali, nobody deserves to endure what you went through. To lose your wife in a falling building, your children attacked by heartless mercenaries... These are no normal circumstances. It was unprecedented. You deserve to be kinder to yourself. I'm telling you, nothing in this world could have prepared you for what you encountered. You experienced an unspeakable destiny and you did what you could in that moment. You're not a magical superhero that can block a bullet in mid air, please, Ali, go easier on yourself. You *must* forgive yourself."

"Forgive *myself*? Why should I indulge in such niceties when my family is not here to live and enjoy the rest of their lives?"

"Ali. If Salma were here to see you now, what would she wish for you? To die in sorrow, or to fight all the way unto the end? The world needs you, please, you must get through this."

"But she is not here... my dear wife, and my poor children. And I will carry this pain with me to whatever heaven or hell awaits me in the afterlife. My Lord has left me, as he left all that remained in my old home. You say the world needs me, but what is the use of a Godless world? Damned in sorrow, there is no certainty in fate, no worthy path to follow, the shell of my former purpose, now broken, worthless and hollow."

"Life is never certain, Ali. Certainty is deadness, just as the only certainty is death. You are going to die one day, for this you can be sure. But before you go, you must give yourself the certitude that you did everything within your power to help this world. Every mortal tastes death, but only some taste life. You know this, Ali, you know this deep down, but your pain clouds your view. Go forth and leave pride behind in what you do, may you know the helping hands extended to you. Regrets weigh on your mind from the heavens. Scorch the shackles of the past through the burning gratitude in your heart. As the skies conspire in your favour, so shall you will see the good results in your work."

"Save me your motivational chatter, Optimism Man. I do not want my head in the clouds. Besides, if you really wanted me to move forward, you would find a way to remove my pain. Instead of telling me to forgive myself, you would wave your magic wand and give me the ability to do so. You say you are a man of vibration, not words, and it is showing in the lack of practicality in which you speak."

The figure closed his eyes and sighed with a gentle smile. He inhaled deeply before he offered his words of guidance: "*Forgiving yourself... begins by forgiving others.* Learn to forgive others by acknowledging their pain. Why? Because when you love the people hardest to love, you will love the most painful corners of yourself."

"You mean... to love my enemy? What kind of feeble sentiment is that?...Didn't you hear what I just said?!"

"Forgiving others is not a sign of giving up, it is an act of receiving" continued the figure.

"What I want is impossible to receive."

"You may not have what you want, but know that you are very much needed."

"I am sorry," Ali bemoaned, "I've let so many people down. My pain is too great, I am of no use to anyone anymore."

"What does pain feel like?"

...

"Hopelessness." Ali replied, almost in a shameful whisper.

"Describe it, what does hopelessness *feel* like?"

"There is no fire in my belly, no beauty to spark my flame. There is only a dead weight; a piercing, dense, sadness."

"What else?" the figure persisted.

"My heart feels betrayed, saddened. Like there is no life left."

"And what does that do to you?"

"My mind is lethargic, no longer connected to the source of motivation that once coloured my work. My thoughts lack the contrast of even black or white. My ideas are murky in an insignificant grey."

"And how does that make you feel?"

"I feel like I am no longer the man I used to know... I don't like to think about it."

"You feel this weight in your body, as a shackle that pulls you away from the sun, behind the dark clouds of your mind."

"And now there is no more sun, just sad, grey, rainy days." Ali lamented.

"The sensation of pain has clouded even your vision. I see no shackle on you."

"What do you see?" asked Ali, his resignation grounding him in a bemused willingness to learn.

"I see a treasure chest. It is large... *heavy* , with thick, steel doors. Its cubic corners lodged in your very gut."

"Well, you won't find anything inside." he said in a defeated tone.

"Why don't we find out?"

"Sure, where's the key?" Ali's cynicism now overriding.

"The key to your treasure chest awareness."

It was all now too much. Ali let out a deep sigh and bowed his head. "This is excruciating..."

"Stay with me, Ali. Remember, all the problems you see in the world stem from man's inability to sit alone, honestly and aware, with himself."

"Alright... so I am aware, and honestly alone. Now what?"

"Not so fast, Ali. I want you to be in the same state of awareness as you are when you're meditating. Remember, *breathing without thinking*, then observe whatever arises."

Ali sighed, "Sure" he replied.

"Now sit up straight."

"Alright."

"Now just breathe. That's all you need to do. Remember, letting go is just breathing without thinking. Breathe and observe the feelings in your body. Relax. Turn the key of your treasure chest by listening to the weight in your gut."

"Listening?"

"Make note of the feeling. Lower your ear to the knots in your body. Hear how they twist and turn your anxiety-ridden belly. I want you to be discerning. Scrutinise the nature of the sadness, feel how it scavenges the life force from your core. Dispel the robber who devours your sacred vault. Their persistence is fuelled by your resistance. Don't let them run away with your energy. Ignore them no more!"

Ali, a veteran of the mind and now student of the heart, followed this guidance, sitting feelingly until the late evening.

"Reveal your pain," the voice echoed encouragingly, "let it rise to the surface."

Ali's sitting posture was discontented. He grimaced as he felt an amalgamation of self-hatred and despair bubbling upwards, closer to the surface of his volcanic experience.

"Feel the pain," the voice chimed relentlessly:

"Make love to the pain, dissolve the chemical residue of the past!"

Ali groaned, feeling a subtle lump of acidic lethargy in his core, "How?"

"Can you accept what you're feeling right now?"

"No!"

"What are you resisting, Ali?"

"What do you mean?!"

"Are you able to identify the emotions that manifest as physical sensations in your body?"

"Ugh. Why would I pay attention to them?" Ali complained, trying hard to dispel the thought.

"Is there any resistance to being *you*?"

"*Yes*. I don't *want* to feel weak... I'm ashamed of how I feel. I'm so terribly ashamed. I miss who I used to be!"

"Accept all that you're feeling. It's okay to feel shame. It's okay to be anxious. You're allowed to worry. Sadness is a natural expression. If your great-great-grandparents never worried, you wouldn't be here today. Give yourself permission for a moment to just *feel* whatever your senses tell you. Then you will witness something quite unique."

"What?" murmured Ali, barely willing to articulate his words.

"Soon you will discover that these feelings are comparable to morse code. They deliver a fleeting message to your system... And all they ask is that you *listen* and acknowledge them *fully*."

"So I just have to *feel* them fully? Is that all?"

"Sit with your feelings, have the courage to feel them in their entirety. Then after a while, watch and see as they mature like a soft, sweet wine. You must heed the messages of your feelings, they are desperate to relay their story in their entirety. From their causal beginning, to their present state and soon their educational end. Embrace them fully and you shall feel them pass. Their emotional charge cannot last forever."

Ali squeezed his eyes tighter, lasering in on his entrenched grief. "What messages? How long?"

"Patience, Ali. Know that all emotions have their advantages. Accept them. Relax into them to alchemise their wisdom. Be your own alchemist."

Ali remained focused as the being continued to guide him: "There is a trauma that clouds the capacity of your intelligent body. Purge yourself and resurrect the beauty of your intuitive nature. When the feeling clears, it will be as if your mind has room to think again. When you become your true, unhindered self again, you'll sense how to approach your path. You will feel subtleties and start trusting yourself to act instinctively. Soon, you will know the right thing to do and say. But to gain this clarity, you must first make peace with your pain. Only by walking through your fire will you find your light. Emotional pain is temporary, avoidance is unnecessary. Whatever you resist persists."

Ali bellowed in despair "I... I feel a sadness in my chest and an aching knot of angst in my gut. My world is so unpleasant."

"Keep going, Ali. Step into the pain and draw out its charge. Accept whatever you are feeling by drawing your full attention to it. Your attention will turn the key to unlock your treasure chest. Open up the door and unmask that which is buried inside the light of your awareness. *Feel* fully as the darkness burns to ashes, revealing your wisdom gems. Such is the furnace of the philosopher's stone."

Ali sat abidingly, pushing through the discomfort and focusing his attention on the deluge of sensations that weaved and churned throughout his body. He turned his awareness inward, gradually increasing the volume on his residual traumas. Old memories charged with fear, anger, guilt and shame were confronted with a new tacit awareness. Becoming ever more vivid, they overwhelmed his system with their absolute potential.

"Grieve, Ali... resist your pain no more!"

"I don't understand... all I feel is sadness, I'm consumed with sadness."

"Have patience and accept what you are feeling. Embrace your sadness."

"Why?!"

"To be your true self you must accept yourself. To accept yourself you must forgive yourself. Do you understand? Accept yourself as you are, now, no matter how you are feeling."

"But it's unbearable, it feels wrong. I can barely sit still."

"Celebrate all that arises in you. Then everything you label as 'wrong' will vanish. Confront your negative emotions with a state of love and acceptance. Let go of your resistance."

"I feel grief... a deep aching."

"Then grieve. And breathe... yes, breathe all the way in. Feel every expression of your emotions, give them the attention they require. As you breathe in, feel as though you are pulling your emotions upwards through your body. As you breathe out, feel as if you are pushing the emotions outwards from your body..." the being lowered his voice and closed his eyes. He hovered his glowing arms over Ali, as if to offer a helping, healing hand.

Ali obeyed his instructions. Sitting honestly with his emotions as they tormented him turbulently. The minutes drifted into hours as he mastered his preoccupation with breath. Embracing his feelings, he visualised all manner of angst being expelled from his carcass through an outward exhalation. Desperation fuelled his endurance to overcome his discomfort. He silently prayed for mercy and respite from this painful end... but it never came easily.

"It's not your fault" the voice encouraged.

"Argh..." Ali wailed, struggling to maintain his breath.

"Repeat my words."

"What words?"

"Tell me it's not your fault."

"It's not my fault," Ali echoed "it's... not my fault."

"Good... keep breathing. Grieve away your sadness and accept yourself for who you are. Your emotions do not define you. Acknowledge them and receive their wisdom. Feel them come to pass... Now tell me, what are you holding onto that's preventing you from feeling at peace?"

"I'm... so angry."

"You're not angry, but there is anger in you. You're contracting. Breathe, Ali, and loosen your core. Breathe and sit up straight, breathe and open up your heart...What else can you sense?"

Ali followed the guidance obediently. He breathed deeply, relaxing his shoulders until they loosened and melted into his upper arms. He maintained a penetrative focus as if drilling for oil. Inward, deeper, yet all the while feeling; listening to the intense knot of angst which lay above his core.

"I... feel anger at myself... I feel so much... shame" Ali wept in despair. "This isn't working... I feel worse, how can I make it stop?!"

"You're making progress. Keep going. Go deeper, Ali. What do you see?"

"I see the hopelessness of my future.... I feel that I daren't wish for days of joy or a life of meaning."

"But why not?"

"Because I don't deserve it! I lost my wife and failed my children. Why should I ever see a warm and joyful day, when they are cold and dead in the ground?"

"You speak of guilt."

"I feel..."

"What?... What do you feel?"

"I feel like I don't deserve to be alive!" Ali cried out, his composure ruptured by a ravaging sea of sorrow. Tears, from long ago, freed themselves from the depths of Ali's soul.

"It's okay, Ali... breathe deeply now," the figure soothed him.

Ali soundlessly wept. "I'm sorry... I'm so sorry. Please forgive me. I never meant for this to happen..." he repeated, lamenting in despair.

The luminous being stood sensitively beside the grieving Ali. He saw his iridescent outline reflecting a mirror image back at him in a line of tears now accumulating on the prison floor. He gazed down at Ali empathetically and told him, "You may direct your apology to nobody else but yourself. Your family; Salma, little Michael and Elizabeth, never blamed you for what happened. Not for one moment."

Ali looked up at his celestial friend, his eyes swollen, his tears blurring the majestic glow. Wiping his tears away, mesmerized by the anodyne light emanating from the being's angelic eyes, he asked him "How do you know?"

"I know only of the knowledge in your heart. Your knowledge is my knowledge, my love is your love, your pain is my pain. You gave life to me through your love for Salma, through your selfless service to others, through your writings, the works of which you will come to remember. Know that it is you who helped me touch the wisdom of the heavens, so my radiant presence shall shine eternally beside you, guiding you to your truth. Remember, Ali, no truthful man walks through life entirely alone."

Ali gazed through the shimmering light, feeling sedated by the comforting presence of the figure. His tears ceased as he recomposed himself. "Salma could never bear to see me upset", he muttered, continuing to bereave his pain.

"Realise this as you begin to awaken. Come back to yourself, feel yourself at your core."

"What is wrong with me? Why have I lost sight of who I am?"

"Your consciousness has been captured by a signifier of shame. But really, your pain is nothing but the ego itself. In other words, your own self-image tells you that you are somehow defective."

"A signifier of shame?..."

"Once you accepted this self-image, you failed to see its perilous indoctrination."

"Why?"

"Because your sadness caused you to lose touch with your faith. And when you lost touch with your faith, you began to look at yourself through the ego. The ego that feeds on the necessity of survival. The ego that morphs into fictitious facets of defectiveness, lack and ugliness. But you must recognise, Ali, that whatever image makes you feel ashamed of yourself is a lie; is simply not true."

Ali composed his thoughts, "How do I escape this? I'm tired of feeling so worthless."

"The only escape is to keep repeating the question, 'Who am I?'...realise that the 'I' cannot be captured in the illusory signifier of shame that can then be released."

"How is that so?"

"Because once you accept the truth that you are free; formless, and that you are pure light, how could any of those things be true? You are a walking, breathing, self-aware flower in the desert of the Universe; you are divine! When you recognize this, when you internalise this mantra, the whole ego will fall away, as you become aware of your true divine nature."

"So my guilt, my pain, my negative emotions... what are they, really?"

"They are an offshoot of a biological mind that is always trying to *become* something it can feel proud of. You may feel humble in your guilt, but know that guilt is nothing but the sibling of pride. This is also an illusion, a psycho-structure, albeit a very painful one. Once you recognize that the pain you feel comes from a false belief or an egoic effort; once that false belief is unearthed, the pain has no choice but to alchemise; to dissolve and turn into wisdom. As you gain meaning from suffering, the suffering will be no more."

"But how can an illusion affect my physical body?"

"It is only a matter of time before a negative repetitive thought matures into a negative internal emotion projected into your physical body. The bodily feeling then generates thoughts of like-nature, keeping you trapped in this karmic loop. But the more one has advanced in the vibration of love and can turn that love inward, the less power these obstacles of negativity and limitation can affect one. When you realise that you are *the* supreme consciousness that cannot be known by another and cannot be shamed, you understand that there is no other. It is breaking free of the ego container that is falsely felt as your whole consciousness."

"Supreme consciousness... this is what the other being spoke of in my dream last night."

"It was no dream, Ali. Your experience was very real."

"He said that every book that has been written, has been written by the same author. What does that mean? That I must know myself, deep down, and find some deified creator inside?"

"Almost... Every being is a manifestation of one kind of bliss - a unique bliss that can only be known by the true self. We refer to this term as *'know* thy self', however, even this is not correct. For if we talk of *knowing* the self, there must be two selves, one a *'knowing* self' and the one which is *'known'*. But the state of realisation is simply *being* oneself, not knowing anything. The *process* of knowing oneself, is simply being oneself, not knowing anything, or becoming anything... are you following?"

"Not fully..."

"The supreme self does not *'know'* anything, especially not knowledge of signifiers of language, as words are simply a labelling of the material plane that is itself illusory. The supreme *real* self has no interest in knowing the illusion, it is free from the illusion!"

"But the ego, the pain; the lie, is trapped in the illusion?"

"Correct, Ali. The ego is only the desire to become, within this material illusion, a *somebody*. Someone without a shaming signifier that is creating one's traumas. But when one is free of this constraint, one is free of the finite. Free of birth and death; and of all the possibilities of being captured and limited, liberated fully into the 'deified' self as you speak. But to do this, there must be a complete absence of identification with the ego, a complete annihilation with any identification of the animate, or any signifier, including the body, mind, and of all the images of this material plane. This is what you achieve in the tranquillity of meditation. It's to realise that none of the images in your mind pertain to the *self* that is forever unborn, and deathless. Know that you are *that*. Here and now, tomorrow, and forevermore!"

"That's... something I need time to process. I know what you're saying is true. I know that I'm hostage to my thoughts and trapped in my feelings. These emotions are just difficult to relinquish when I have felt this way for so long."

"Take your time, Ali. For while the mind may consciously believe, the body which is the subconscious manifestation of the mind will require more time. If your conscious mind is a puddle, your subconscious mind is an ocean. Be mindful of the reality of your predicament, know that each day is an opportunity for worthy improvement. Feel shame, but know that you do not deserve to feel shame. Know that it is there, welcome it even, but remember to *repeat* your truth to yourself, no matter what happens, as you commit yourself to meditation, and allow it to pass. Everything in the material realm is transient."

"What truth do I repeat?"

The majestic figure raised his hands and placed his palms in a gesture of prayer. He closed his eyes, his brows fluorescent from the glow of his fingertips. "I'M LIGHT" he softly declared:

> "I'M TRUTH,
>
> I'M LOVE, DIVINE.
>
> THIS BODY-MIND,
>
> A DREAM OF MINE".

"Repetition... discipline," whispered Ali, "repetitive spiritual discipline."

"All of your life" continued the being, "you have guided other people on how to master their spiritual path through your writings and how to surmount the difficulties which arise from life's lessons. Now, from this night onwards, you can speak with authority as you are about to succeed in surmounting your own tests. You shall pass triumphantly, resolute and unafraid. That is your purpose."

"Purpose..." Ali thought, "something worth doing..."

"With these things in mind, tell me – how do you feel?"

Ali felt challenged by the encouraging words. "I feel... hope" he reluctantly disclosed.

The figure looked searchingly into Ali's eyes as if to assess the authenticity of his words. "Well then," he said, posturing upright, "my work here is done."

"Done? What do you mean, where are you going? What should I do now?"

"Live by your words. *Listen to the silence...*"

Ali gazed longingly at the figure as he slowly faded into a soft gaseous, technicolour cloud. He dissolved from the ground upward, disappearing back into the nothingness from which he came.

Alone, Ali stared blankly into the wall for a moment "I don't have to feel this way" he told himself.

The voice, still trailing, *"Put both hands on your heart."*

Ali spun around to see nobody but himself and the dark, four walls. As he lifted his hands, they were immediately weighed back down, counterbalanced by the thick metal shackles, moored like a ship, heavy on his thin emaciated wrists.

"Breathe deep into your heart" the voice guided.

Ali followed.

"Now think, Ali... what do you feel proud, or grateful for, that your heart has guided you to feel, to do, or to say?"

Ali closed his eyes and scanned his mind, searching for a meaningful memory; a heart-warming event from a life not so long ago. He recollected his days as a teacher in the struggling primary school of his hometown, the happiness of watching his children as they played with their friends. Going off-topic in after school classes, acting out all kinds of stories, he reminisced taking the minds of the children on a magical journey, a momentary respite from their poverty-stricken lives. He felt a warm vibration of love wash over him. He remembered the children sharing food with each other, food he provided each night with the modest earnings from his books. He kept his hands on his heart and breathed deeply, his eyes smiling as he relaxed in melancholic memories.

The voice calmly continued "You didn't have to *earn* this heart... It was *given* to you. Something loved you enough to give you the gift of life. Now, always remember, first comes the sensation, then comes emotion. From the emotion, *thought* arises. See this, observe this, and dissolve the looping chains that erode your mind."

Ali continued his meditative plight, still suffering side effects from confronting his feelings. He could feel their charge gradually dwindling.

He reminded himself that he could only overcome pain by facing and accepting it fully. He recognised that his inability to overcome shame mirrored his inability to dispel his pride. He realised that, while he was not at fault for what happened, he was at fault for holding onto the shame it caused him - a shame that shaded his light. Above all, Ali knew that even if he were at fault, only humble forgiveness could begin to make things right.

Through the teachings of his heart, Ali learnt that love was the only medicine powerful enough to heal the parasite of shame. As he grappled with the grip of guilt, he saw guilt not as a menacing monster, but a conscious child, afraid, in need of a bedtime story, much like the children in his school.

Ali evaluated the emotional residues of his past with greater wisdom. He felt the twisted knots of angst in his stomach begin to loosen, as if they had a little mercy on him, as if to reward his attention he had now given them. In the early hours of the morning, his body was exhausted from processing all the emotions that were buried below. But through it all, he felt gratitude for his new perspective: of learning a better way to deal with pain.

Ali rested in humility that night, burning with love.

CHAPTER

6

n the less early hours of that morning, the guard arrived once more, but this time, carrying an even greater array of goods than the previous day. Ali had just woken up from his cataclysmic night of adventure. Still fatigued and battle-worn, he wiped the sleep from his eyes. The guard lay down a tray with a melange of seasonal fruits and a large pot of steaming tea, ready to be decanted into a small crystal cup. He reached around his leather satchel and carefully selected two piles of paper, one filled with texts from varied sources and the other pile, blank. He placed them on the floor, this time more attentively, paying particular attention to ensure the edges sat flush, before carefully placing a pen on top.

Ali watched with suspicion, surprised at the increased level of favour he was receiving. Eager to immerse himself forthwith, he glanced over at the top sheet of paper and spotted some unfamiliar names on the new scholarly content. He sensed the guard avoiding eye contact and wondered if it was a result of their interaction the day before, or whether he was just following orders.

The guard stood back, fidgeting nervously with another sheet of paper as he attempted to procure it from his bag. Ali assumed this was the agreement he'd been asked to sign.

The guard surreptitiously glanced over at Ali, quickly averting his gaze to the floor when Ali caught his eye. Bemused, Ali detected a sense of ambivalence within him, "Is he too afraid to speak to me again?" he thought, suddenly feeling guilty, aware of the impact his decisions had on others. This sense of guilt surprised him, throwing him into a conflicted mix of empathic confusion.

The guard let out a heavy sigh, spun his heels and began to walk away.

"*Wait*" blurted Ali.

The guard froze with his back half-turned as he postured to leave. Ali was unaware of the relief now detailed on his face.

"Hmm..." Ali struggled to find the correct words. He picked up the first sheet of paper and asked "why does the Ministry want me to translate old stories of Adam and Eve?"

"I don't know," the guard snapped bluntly, perhaps anticipating a different inquiry "I can't read Ancient Greek."

"I see..." replied Ali, "well, I guess there's nothing else then."

Acutely disappointed, the guard resumed his walk towards the door.

Now wrestling with discontent, Ali was quick to devise another strategy to extend his daily encounter. As the guard reached for his keys, in perfect synchronicity, they broke the silence together:

Guard: "I had an argum-"

Ali: "Look I'm sorry I-"

They both paused to give the other a chance to speak.

"You had a what?" asked Ali.

"I had an argument with my wife last night" said the guard, surprised at his own candour.

"About what?"

Clasping his keys back on his belt, the guard continued, "Ever since I told her about our encounter, she's been hounding me about my job; how I make a living for our family, and the way I am forced to treat you." He felt relieved, finally able to offload a heavy burden that was playing on his mind.

"And why is she so upset?"

"Because she knows of your work, Ali. Like everyone else, she was saddened by the fallacious propaganda surrounding your death. I couldn't resist but to tell her of our interaction. Who else can I talk to about my days other than my *wife*? I tell her *everything*, but this job causes so much tension in our relationship...". "You see, I want to be a great writer, someday... And my wife... she helps me with my writing, and when she heard that I was your captor, she looked at me in a way that I've never seen before... as if I were sent on a mission by Satan. She made me feel like some tragic hypocrite, who doesn't even believe in his own words."

"I did not know that you were an aspiring writer, young man," said Ali, surprised. "So, is that why you wanted to know the meaning of the last passage from my book?"

"I guess..."

"Tell me, what do you like to write about?"

"I want to write about God, religion and the purpose of man."

"Ah... well, good luck with that," said Ali, patronisingly. "God is dead, what are you going to write about, his obituary?"

The guard was visibly saddened by the cutting response, "I can't believe what I'm hearing" he said.. "aren't you the one who dedicated your whole life to the same recourse?"

Ali noticed the change in the guard's demeanour "Okay, look, I'm sorry" he said, now trying to retract the damage. "I didn't mean to be rude... it's just... this cell has made me bitter, and my impending death a little more honest."

"Impending death? What do you mean? Just sign these papers, we can get you medical attention, you don't need to be in here anymore."

Ali smiled as he looked up towards the small window. "My time here is done, young man. I've become weak and delirious. These days, there is nothing I want more than to pass peacefully."

"I won't accept this! I'm going to get you medical help... but... I'm confused. Just last night I heard you talking to someone, you sounded like you were convincing yourself of something. There was a glimmer of purposefulness in your voice, I thought, maybe you were deciding to take up some new path?"

"Ah... I'm sorry you had to hear that." Ali lowered his gaze. "What you heard was nothing but a generous consolation that arrives for every old, sad man. When one's prayers whisper repeatedly at the gates of an ineffectual heaven for so long, it's only a matter of time before some angel responds out of pity, to calm an aching, dying mind."... "Also, I must confess, I'm sorry for dismissing your inquiry the way I did yesterday. Admittedly, you caught me a little off-guard with your proud recital of a miserable translation of my words. My rebuttal was nothing but a projection of my own insecurity and anger onto you."

"I accept your apology... I just wish that-" the guard stopped in his tracks.

"You wish what, boy?"

"I wish that one day I can learn to speak like you. When you talk, it's as if you already know what to say. There are a thousand stories in your mind... it's as if you can pause time, and take your time before preparing your response."

"Well... I've had a long time to think."

"You did it again..." the guard replied, frustrated "my wife is always telling me to pursue my writing career. But she doesn't know that I don't have the confidence. Besides, the way you speak is more poetic than anything I could write. I'm so ambitious, but I don't stand a chance against *naturals* like yourself."

Ali looked suspiciously at him, "Young man, you live in a time where there is an immense pressure for you to process so much information - too much information. Unlike previous generations, there is a far greater chance for your mind to be confused and intellectually collapse under these conditions. With all this data, it becomes very hard for one to really decide what they believe in, or what's even worth writing about. It's this lack of conviction that you equate to a low level of confidence in yourself. Go a little easier on yourself. It's all about knowing what is and is not useful for *you*, keep this in mind and your writing path will become easier to find. But back to the matter at hand... are you only saying all of this to flatter me? To make me accept your proposition?"

"Look, I appreciate your words of advice" continued the guard, "I can get into a lot of trouble for speaking to you like this. I'm just... under extreme pressure to return this agreement with your signature on it."

"But you have to understand, if I sign those papers, I'll be signing away the integrity of my name and all my works."

"I thought you didn't care about all of that!" said the guard, surprised. "What with this nonchalant attitude of yours... besides, didn't you ask me to burn all of your books?"

Ali looked over at the guard, impressed by his response, "That was pretty smooth, see? You're not so bad with words! Perhaps you should give yourself more credit."

"Thank you" the guard smiled and nervously looked away.

It was the first time Ali saw him smile. The first time Ali cared about his mood, and the first time he was fully present with him. "You know, my wife also used to help me with my writing. If it weren't for her, I wouldn't have written a single book."

"Really? Why is that?"

"Well... if it makes you feel better, I'll let you in on a little tip about becoming a writer."

"Tell me."

"Why don't you sit down and I'll tell you?"

"You know I can't be seen talking to you" the guard began to grow increasingly anxious.

"Oh, come on! Just tell them you were trying to persuade me to sign the papers. Stay and talk with me for a while and I'll sign whatever it is you want me to sign."

"Really?!" the guard said eagerly, as he reached into his bag, before stopping to regain his composure.

"Yes, but only after we talk…" Ali said with a half smile.

"That's blackmail!" the guard complained.

"Is it? Or would you really just be denying a dying man's last wish?"

"…Will you sign the paper if we talk?" the guard pleaded.

"Yes, you have my word."

"Do you promise?"

"I *promise*, young man."

The guard sighed, still suspicious as to whether to trust Ali "Okay, but only for a short while" he said, dusting off a comfortable spot on the floor. He sat down and rested his back against the stone wall, flinching as the cold shot through his spine.

"Do you ever wonder why they chose you to watch over me?" Ali asked.

"I already know why."

"Why?"

"Because I never missed a shot in my training."

"Really? Not one?"

"No. I'm a sharpshooter, my sniper is in the back" the guard said pointing down the corridor "I also scored the highest in my regiment in all of my exams."

"Sharpshooter, eh?"

"Yup. You see this page?" the guard said, waving the contract in the air…"If you hung this from a line, I could take two shots from a mile away, and you would only see one bullet hole in the page."

"Why, because you missed a shot?"

"No! Because both bullets go through the same hole - ahh"… the guard realised the joke, "very funny Ali… now, tell me… what's this writing tip?"

"Well, the tip is related more to my secret as a writer. And my secret is that… I've never actually finished reading any one book from start to finish."

"What? You?! Ali, the great philosopher... How is that so?"

"Well, to be honest, I always found reading books a little bit boring... So many chapters are filled with backstories and extraneous information that dull the juicy insights where, by the time I reach the main point, I'm too exhausted to even recognise it! You see, if you want to write, you must respect the reader's time. Your words must spark across the page as if the reader ignites them with their eyes. A good writer must provide life-changing morals to a story, but with enough self-awareness to make fun of them, because everything is contextual in life. In reality, this balance is hard to find, and that's why I could never become submerged in a topic from start to finish. I think this is why so many readers were able to resonate with my work. I liked to simplify things."

"Why simplify?"

"Because people are busy... and you are supposed to do the work *for* them as a writer, not get them to work for you!"

"So what makes good writing? Let me make some notes..."

"Writing is very much akin to composing music. There are crescendos and there are crashes, there are slow points and there are fast points. There is a range of tone, but not too much to make one dizzy, and not too little to make one bored. Some songs are better when played in the artist's order within the whole album. Similarly, some chapters come alive only when you read the one after it. Sometimes, you notice new things from the same piece when you pay closer attention. Other times you have a different experience depending on what's happening in your life at that moment. A great song is one that people can enjoy time and time again, regardless of the era or the context. Likewise, a great book is one that is enjoyed by many generations of readers. Lastly, it's not about how many songs you have in your library, but how much you enjoy the ones you have. In the same way, it's not about how many books you've read, but how you integrate their wisdom into your daily life."

"I see, Ali... but what I don't get is, how do you know so much? How were you able to write so much - so well - if you said that all you did was superficially skim over everything you read?"

"Because really, once you start getting too deep on the most important topics; like purpose, God, spirituality and so forth... you really miss the whole point. That's the problem with all these writings of grandeur, they leave the reader at risk of drowning, when really, you must always stay on the surface."

"But why? What's so good about staying on the surface?"

"Because the truth should be so obvious that it hits you in the face. Truth is strengthening, empowering, it does not hide under impenetrable layers of obscurity. And what most writers will never confess, is that they really write to impress... instead, they should sacrifice the opportunity of sophistication and focus on what the main purpose of their book should be."

"And what's that?"

"The main purpose of every book should be to extract the light from the reader's mind and project it back to them in the form of words".

"What does that mean? What light?"

"Well, it depends... Tell me, have you ever lost yourself in a really good book?"

The guard thought for a moment "Yes, I love fiction stories - stories that have a meaning... especially stories that could be true. Those are the ones I really lose myself in."

"And why is that?"

"Because, well..." the guard thought for a moment before he continued, eager to provide a meaningful answer. "Sometimes, when I read a story, I imagine that I am the main character... And I guess I enjoy stories where I feel that the main character is some ideal, brave, version of me and that, if put in the same situation, I would make the same choices of the character. And really, it feels like I'm learning about myself when I get lost in a good book. It feels like I'm learning from a faraway journey, and by the end of it, I'm left savouring the last few pages... before the story inevitably finishes and I'm left with some new insights, some quasi-experiential knowledge that I could perhaps apply to my own life... and become closer with that ideal that I aspire to be."

"That is a magnificent description, young man. You should write about that someday."

"Well, maybe... But I feel like I'm trying to describe something that isn't tangible... It's frustrating. It's not only this but much more. There's a certain *feeling* I get when I'm engrossed in a good book. I'm trying to crack the code of what it is... the secret ingredient that makes me yearn to turn the pages. It's almost as if I'm *searching* for something inside the text... yes, that's what it feels like. When I'm lost in a book, in a story, it feels like I'm searching for... I don't know... *something* that I don't even know, but I know that once I *get* it, once I realise it, I will feel more complete, more at one with myself. Does that make sense?"

"That makes perfect sense."

"Can you put into words what I'm describing?"

"You see, we are all craving some connection with that which is higher than ourselves. We're searching for a connection with something we feel that we've lost. But the problem with describing it with *words* is that one may read too much into them and that would be a mistake. If you want to write about anything worth writing about, all you can do is paint with words, so the message that's being conveyed is non-verbal. Really, the ultimate connection you are seeking you will not find in rational thought processing. It's as simple as that."

The guard thought for a moment, "That's interesting" he said. "So is this why you wrote about God? Was it God who said those mysterious words I read in your books?"

Ali shook his head and turned away dismissively.

"What's wrong, Ali?"

Ali remained silent.

The guard persisted, "I must say, I think it's a perfectly reasonable question."

"Of course it's a reasonable question, it's an excellent question."

"So what's the problem? Are you angry at God, or something?"

"The problem is..." Ali began, the pain etched on his face. "This word *God* has become so heavily loaded that it has lost all meaning."

"What do you mean?"

Ali glanced up at the window, hesitating as he struggled to find an answer. He was uncertain as to whether his answer had changed in recent years, or if he was no longer sure of what he felt or believed.

"Tell me," he said, confronting the guard eye-to-eye, "What kind of God would let a soldier shoot my daughter in the face?"

The guard was taken aback "I don't know... I-"

"Or let me put it another way. What kind of *God* would let me bury my sleeping son alive? Or crush my wife's bones beneath the weight of a falling building?"

The guard was dumbstruck.

"Is this a God that works in mysterious ways?" Ali pressed on. "Actually, forget about my family for a moment. I appreciate that we're a war-torn anomaly... What about the people who are born with or develop some form of chronic illness? Those poor souls who live with invisible pains that no doctor can diagnose; the kind of pain that outsmarts even the most addictive of painkillers. Why would God place this fate on someone? Is this another one of his *tests* that he'll explain in heaven, where we'll all laugh about it and reminisce for an eternity? Are my wife and children sitting happily on a throne with God in heaven right now? Did they all smile in unison when God told them that their gruesome death was part of their divine journey, something that they now *understand*? Am I the unreasonable, sinful, ignorant one for not wanting my family to be the angelic students of a scholastic God? Am I going to hell for not believing in God's plans, his mysterious tests? Do I not have a say in all this, of how I feel about his sick games?"

The guard felt ashamed. Raising his eyebrows as he searched for a response, trying to find the correct degree of sensitivity to console his captive.

"You asked me a question and I gave you an honest response", Ali scathed sarcastically. "The problem with God is that he raises more questions than he answers. Tell me, honestly, I would love to hear your thoughts on this, young man. I'm all ears" said Ali, raising his arms up in the air, gesturing for a response.

"I don't know, I wouldn't be able to say…" the guard refrained from making eye contact, trying to buy some time whilst he mused for the right reply. "Well… you know, there's also the theory of reincarnation," he said gingerly, hoping not to offend.

"Reincarnation... and karma?" echoed Ali.

"Yes, karma".

"And what about karma?"

"Well, they say what you receive in this lifetime is a result of your actions and choices in a previous life. It's the belief that..." the guard cut himself short, realising the ineffectuality of his argument. "I'm sorry. I know how little this makes sense"

"You're right, it doesn't make sense. Not to me, anyway. But look, you don't need to be sorry, I've thought about this myself before - this concept of karma... there's just one thing I can't seem to understand about it".

"What's that?"

"In all the years I've sat in this cell, alone with my thoughts, you can't imagine how many times I've dreamt of retribution for the evil soldiers who carry out horrendous acts with no remorse or sense of shame. Those subhuman... animals who have no discernment between man, woman or child. It's as if they have no conscience at all, it's like evil is ingrained within them. Ignorance is their nature, and there is no repenting for these kinds of men... if you can call them men. And there is my point about karma, my hoping and wondering if they will ever be punished not in this life, but in the next. The concept of heaven and hell has been lost on me for a long time, for reasons I mentioned before... I'm saying...". Ali had lost his momentum, "I'm sorry. I seem to have lost my train of thought."

"It's okay" the guard reassured, eager to grasp the bottom line of Ali's point. "I know it's difficult to talk about. You were saying that you didn't quite understand the concept of karma, or reincarnation."

"Yes, as I was trying to put myself in the shoes of God, or whatever demi-God is tasked with administering karma to each person... I thought of the legitimacy of punishing someone in their next life... when I say next life, I mean their memory wiped, and then bang, they're born a baby, doomed to a life of suffering, the reason of which they'll never know. I tried to reason with it, but I could never understand or come to a conclusion on how any punishment like that can be just."

"But what's not to understand? The whole point of karma is that you experience the exact same pain that you inflicted on others", the guard confidently rebuted.

"But, to *not* know what you're being punished for? It doesn't make sense to me. Not after what I have seen. It just doesn't make sense. Not for an intelligent creator. Not the one I know of. It just reminds me of a big, sick game. Who knows, maybe that's what life is, the creator's big, sick game..."

"So what is the creator that you know of? Do you at least have any new philosophy on life? Has anything you've read stood the test of time?" the guard quizzed incessantly, attempting to savour some meaning out of the existentialist Ali.

"As I mentioned, I don't like to delve too much into one topic, or 'philosophy'. This is not out of disrespect to any one author, but rather because I respect all authors, all philosophers. They are simply speaking of what resonates as true to them, and who am I to critique another for that? I take the same approach with my religious education. For example, although I do not regard myself a Muslim, I love the Islamic tradition. The Quran is the deepest I have dived in a single book and nothing else compares. The symbolic meanings behind its stories, its depth and mathematical beauty are unparalleled. The quality of teachings cleverly compressed in each sentence and Surah can be extracted out to construct entire books of their own. I also enjoy teachings which mirror the messages of the Quran, albeit in a plainer form, such as the peaceful way of the Chinese Tao; of being at one with the flow of creation that runs through you. Or the Hebrew idioms that make up the parables that Moses used in his prophecies concerning the birth, life, death, and resurrection of Jesus Christ."

"So, do you *still* regard yourself as a Christian?"

"Look, young man, take all I say with a pinch of salt. I appreciate I may not make much sense, so forgive me. My mind is languishing and my memory is decaying." Ali's exhaustion was now beginning to reveal itself. It took him twice as long to think and catch his breath.

"I've been labelled a Christian as a child and I never contested it," he continued, "but it's the adoption of labels that have caused many problems in this world. In reality, all beliefs share a deep, unified connection with each other. If we could only be brave enough to resist the temptation of embellishing our identity with labels, we'd live more peacefully. Labels are the problem; words create the separation from the indescribable."

"Okay, so if you have no *label*, then what do you believe in? You *must* believe in... something?" the guard persisted.

"I believe in the golden line of truth I have found in my years of *skim* reading." Ali said jokingly, pouring his first cup of tea, "Why don't you get yourself a glass?"

"I'm okay, thank you. Tell me, what did you find? What is the golden line of truth?"

Ali looked up, allowing the guard's question to hover in the light morning air. "Well, that line depends on who you are. Tell me first, have you lived truly?"

"Yes, I've always done the right thing, I never strayed from my responsibilities, and I am always true to my word."

"Then you have nothing to worry about. Do you have any more sugar? I've spoken too much..." Ali said matter of fact as he took another sip of his steaming tea.

"But there is one thing..." remembered the guard, "I've never really prayed at a church or a mosque. I barely know the religion of my homeland."

"That's alright, young man. Every land has been a holy land at some point depending on your perspective. It's good to read widely. You don't need to stick rigidly to one particular religion. They are all interrelated".

"So, give me an example. Where is the interrelation?"

Ali scoured his mind until he recalled a fitting parallel, "Take King Cyrus of Persia. Did you know King Cyrus is mentioned in multiple accounts of Christian biblical texts?"

"Okay... Where?"

"2nd Chronicles - Chapter 26: Verse 23: '*Thus says Cyrus, King of Persia, king of all kingdoms of the Earth: God has charged me to build him a house in Jerusalem*'. For this reason, you could say that the God of ancient Persia is the same as the God in the Bible. However, King Cyrus's God was the

God of Zoroastrians whom they called 'Ahura Mazda', or the 'Lord of Fire'"

"So King Cyrus was a Christian?"

"King Cyrus was a Zoroastrian, an ancient Persian religion."

"Oh, sorry, you said..." the guard said, half disbelieving "That's fascinating... but I'll have to look that up."

"Then also look up Revelation 3:14, as further referenced by Jesus, where he calls himself *Amen*, which is said to be derived from the *Egyptian* God of the Sun, Amon."

The guard stared intently at Ali, perplexed but simultaneously curious.

"You see, it's all the same, young man. As Jesus said: '*I have come to bring fire on the Earth*'. Jesus was a Middle Eastern man, whose original name is Yeshua. He was the son of God, or the son of the Sun God. By this means, you could actually say Jesus Christ is the son of Ahura Mazda, the Zoroastrian God."

"But that's... blasphemous, no?"

"Not yet! The three kings who followed the Star of Bethlehem to find baby Jesus were your classic textbook Magi; a caste of Zoroastrian astrologer priests. Jesus' birth was prophesied in the astrological zodiac – the science of which the Persian astrologers pioneered, building upon the wisdom of the Africans and Indians before them."

"Wait, so the three wise men were Persian?"

"Well, at least one of them, wouldn't you say?"

"What was that Persian religion called, Zoroastrian...ism? Did I pronounce that right?"

"Excellently, young man. Zoroaster is the Persian prophet of Zoroastrianism, predating Jesus by about a thousand years. Through Zoroaster's teachings, it is said that we can become close to Ahura Mazda, or God, by looking within and following the path of truth and righteousness. Zoroastrians believe that everything created by God is pure and should be treated with love and respect. This includes the natural environment, so Zoroastrians traditionally do not pollute rivers, land, or the atmosphere. This has caused some to label Zoroastrianism as the first sustainability-minded religion."

"Wow, I wasn't taught about this at all. It's fascinating... but I'm not quite sure about Zoroastrianism relating to the Christian origin story. That seems quite a stretch."

"Don't worry. Many, but not all Christians like to say that these interpretations are wrong and that their religion is the original and only true religion. But in reality, Jesus' nativity story is a direct replica of the Hindu story of Krishna; born to a carpenter and a virgin on December 25th, like Mithras, heralded by a star in the east, like Horus.... performing healing miracles, walking on water and feeding a whole town from a small basket of food, like Buddha... ascending to heaven, like Hercules, Enoch and Elijah. These are examples of the Universe - the whole cosmos - *straining* to give birth to *Sun Gods*; referring to our own unattained, but attainable state."

"And actually," Ali continued, "if you want to recognise any 'holy' country for its contribution to the spiritual development of humanity, then recognise India. Our Indian brothers and sisters were the ones who saved and protected the ancient Persian Zoroastrian manuscripts. The Persians nowadays would not know half of their religious significance if it weren't for the Indians opening their arms to the migrating Zoroastrians during the Islamic succession of Persia. Many of the greatest English translations of ancient Persian religion have been scribed by Indian writers, may God bless them. Speaking of sustainability... lots of sacred content gets recycled and beautifully repurposed like this, depending on the the translators' culture and level of understanding at the time. Then you have *intentional* symbolism, which muddies the waters a little more for casual truth-seekers. For example, the virgins you read about now in westernised mythology and religion? They're not actually meant to represent virgin women, but are rather said to represent the virgin consciousness. There is your food for thought."

"Virgin *consciousness*? So all those depictions of Virgin Mary are some misleading, secret symbolism only some 'truth-seekers' understand? Are you sure, Ali? This is starting to sound a little... uncomfortable."

"The whole world is an offence, and sometimes the truth is uncomfortable. But we must admit to uncomfortable truths and recognise them for what they are if we are to move forward. Besides, I am only a messenger, I learnt this only recently from the texts you gave me from the Vatican library... if that's really where they are from..."

"Well... what else did they say in relation to this virgin consciousness, what does that mean?"

"They say that when consciousness, or let's just say your 'thoughts', are purged and become unstained, there can be an impregnation of the bridegroom - the Christ. This gives birth to the Christ, or 'Christ Consciousness' within you, which can only be born through a virgin mind. Again this is getting too deep, but these texts aren't the first I've heard of this concept - you can find many books on the topic of Christ Consciousness. I think even now, recent depictions are only just catching up with the cryptic wisdom in the Bible."

"What kind of wisdom?"

"As we discover more about ourselves and our psychology, we realise that the Bible is itself a book of psychology, with a symbolic and archetypal understanding of life and meaning. After all, stories and art are the only ways to immortalise complex truths across generations of traditions and social habituations."

"What kind of symbols?"

"'*Jerusalem - which is above, is free and is the mother of us all*', this refers to the heavenly city within each and every one of us. The term 'Mother' in the Bible is used to describe the *spirit* because spirit is known esoterically as a feminine force. Jerusalem, or should I say *consciousness*, represents what is above - the 'mind'; free from all horrific thoughts that we draw from below - the *animal*. The story of Jesus kicking out the sellers and traders out of the holy temple, is said to represent our responsibility to remove material thoughts from our mind when praying, or meditating. You see, I don't mind calling myself Christian, but my understanding of the religion may differ more than most."

"This is unfathomable. It's a lot to take in. You're beginning to change my perception about what I felt I always knew, but still, I'm struggling to believe what you're saying. How do I know these aren't some swindler interpretations from otherwise more literal texts?"

"You don't have to take my word for it. Jesus Chris said himself, *'See ye first the kingdom of heaven, and his righteousness; and all these things shall be added unto you... the kingdom of heaven is within you'*. And he also said, in Mathew 6:22, *'let thine eye be single, and thy whole body shall be filled with Light'*. Now is it just me, or does that sound Buddhist to you? Or was that more of a Zoroastrian teaching?" Ali playfully concluded.

The guard's expression began to morph from that of disbelief to a state of wonder. "Okay... Alright, you've at least made me curious enough to do my own research to *verify* what you are saying."

"But remember to-" Ali began to point out.

"-Stay on the surface. Yes, I know", the guard laughed.

"Very good", said Ali smiling, as he poured himself another cup of tea. "There's never a need to read too deeply into things. After all, Jesus didn't live an exemplary life just to show you how great he was, he wanted to show you how great *you* are!"

"Hah" the guard chuckled contentedly. "Yeah, I guess.. and who was the Persian prophet again?"

"Zoroaster."

"Zoroaster, yes. I bet he would get along quite well with Jesus. It's a shame they never had a chance to meet."

"You can say that again!" exclaimed Ali "'DO NOT PRAY TO ME FOR THE TRUTH!' Spoke Zoroaster 'DO AWAY WITH THE EXTERIOR!

YOU HAVE THE WHOLE EXISTENCE INSIDE OF YOU.

GO STRAIGHT TO THE SOURCE!'" Ali recited, offering his steaming glass of tea up towards the air.

The guard laughed warmly, beaming with delight at Ali's newfound enthusiasm. He settled his gaze on the steam rising up from the tea, watching Ali caress the crystal glass in his hands. They both sat in a serene haze, silently acknowledging the significance of their conversation, gently digesting the theological sustenance now nourishing their thoughts. The current in the air felt subtly electrifying. It was as though Ali's disregard of taboo, combined with the guard's limited patience, had created a space for a new breakthrough to transpire. They sat at opposing sides of the cell, staring through each other, beyond the walls, both detached from the context of their meeting.

"Oh!" The guard jolted, suddenly breaking the silence. "And what was that line in the Islamic holy book, that God or Allah, is closer to you than your jugular vein? That means

God is within you, right?"

"Yes, a fantastic association. Allah's presence permeates you as much as your capacities. For this reason, he is both near you and distant from you. He is near you as much as you can comprehend, he is distant from you as much as your inability to grasp. But-"

"Wait, wait-" the guard interrupted, "can you say that last bit again? He is near you as much as..."

"*Allah is near you as much as you can comprehend, and he is distant from you as much as your inability to grasp.*"

The guard looked down and winced his eyes, as if trying to calculate a complex maths problem. "Distant from you as much as... okay... okay, I think I get it..." he said.

"But be careful with interpreting the Quran" Ali continued "Arabic is an immeasurably complex language that you must first learn before scratching even the surface of the Quran. This world has been fooled into a fear of Muslim men, but really if you were to fear one thing, it is their intellectual capacity. Islamic scholars often have a difficult time simplifying their advanced and highly nuanced concepts to us common folk. Promise me this, young man, if you are serious about understanding life, spend time with scholars of Islam. Ask them about any problem you may be having, and by the end of the conversation, they will leave your mind as placid as a morning stream."

"Okay, I will."

"Will you promise?"

"Yes, Ali, I promise. But tell me, what is this golden line of truth? After everything you've been through, I want to know what *you* believe in. And without digressing, I want to know about this *source*. The *light* or *virgin consciousness* of which you speak. *Simply,* please. Explain it to me in layman's terms, as if I were a five-year old."

Ali chuckled, "Your willingness to learn is very refreshing" he said as he extended his posture against the wall. He gazed once more at the light filtering through the window, as it refracted into thoughts assimilating in his mind. "Okay," he said, looking back toward the guard "I can give you a *simple* metaphor, and this will help you understand the *whole* thing. Would you like that?"

"Yes, and keep it simple" the guard insisted "stay on the *surface.*"

"Ha!" Ali grinned. "Okay... so, think about your clothes".

"My clothes?"

"Yes, your uniform. Answer me this, would you say that those clothes are *you*?"

The guard looked confused. "No," he said, trying to understand where this was leading. "My clothes are *on* me, but they are not *me*."

"Why are they not you?"

"Because clothes are things that I've been given or collected over the years, they are things I possess, but they are not *me*."

"Excellent. Now, how about your memories?"

"Hmm," the guard contemplated, "I think I see where this is going. You're saying that my memories are things I collected over time, and like my clothes, they are not me... but my memories appear to be part of myself?"

"You are very sharp, Mr. Sharpshooter! Now, take the same attitude toward your thoughts".

"But my thoughts are different. I understand what you're saying, however, thoughts are things that come to me in the moment, they're transient things that emanate out of my mind as a representation of who I am."

"Do you not think your thoughts come from your memory?" asked Ali.

"Okay, I see what you're saying. You're saying that if I had different memories, I'd have some kind of different identity, and out of that identity would arise different thoughts?"

"Correct! Now, tell me, what does that mean to you?"

"That my thoughts are... perhaps not so much *me* as I think they are, and really, I have less control over what thoughts cross my mind than I think. This is due to a lack of control over the collection of memories that influence them."

"Astounding comprehension, young man."

"Okay, but remember I asked you to keep this simple. What's your point, here?"

"My point is that what you perceive as being *you*, may not actually be you."

"And so what?"

"This *source*, this *light*, or *virgin consciousness* you ask about, is referring to the *real you*. And one must learn to identify with the light of their awareness, rather than their thoughts if they are to realise who they truly are, if they want to access their full potential."

"Potential for what?"

"To be inspired, to distinguish the truth from the lie. To learn, grow and to evolve."

The guard nodded, "Okay, okay I follow. So I'm the awareness behind my thoughts, not the thoughts themselves... and there is something special about this awareness, that we should give it more thought – no – we should give it more *attention* than we currently do?"

"Exactly correct! See, you're already halfway there." Ali was pleased with his student's response.

"Okay, so deep down, I am the magical, divine, miraculous observing presence that is behind my thoughts... I am the *light* of consciousness... I am the SON OF THE God OF FIRE or something, right?"

Ali laughed in amusement "Yes, young man. You are more than you know! Break the illusion of thought, dissolve the shackles of subjectivity. Carve away at the lies with the chisel of your intellect. Find that impervious golden pillar of truth that awaits behind the conscious light that cannot be denied."

"So it's not a golden *line* of truth..?"

"Pillar, line, whatever you'd like to name the nameless thing."

"Okay, but my question still remains. What is the point of all this? How does this information help me?"

"Great question", said Ali stroking his beard. "to help you do what exactly?"

"To get what I want out of life..."

"But what is it that you want?"

"I want to provide for my wife and children. And I want to do what I love for a living."

"There are many ways to get there. You can be inspired by many things, but if you ask me, there is no better way than to first be in line with the truth of yourself. This is the lightning path. To see yourself as what you are, to give attention to that which is worthy of attention, the invaluable treasure of yourself that is so easily dirtied by life's tests and distractions."

"Yes, but you're not answering my question," the guard was becoming frustrated.

"Patience, young man. You asked me to explain this to you as I would a child. This is why I must go step, by step, very slowly. Now, tell me, what do you love about your job at the moment?"

"My job? Hmm... the target practice, of course!"

"And what's so special about target practice?"

The guard took a moment to conjure his response, "Well... when it comes to training, I've noticed a difference in my attitude compared to that of my comrades."

"And what's that?"

"It's like they have to force themselves to do basic duties throughout their day. They consume all of their willpower capital. They rely on discipline to go about their work. But for me, it's second nature. While I may have to force myself at the offset, once I'm in the middle of a task, I become at one with it... I don't think about what I'm doing, and it's never really a chore for me."

"And that's when you never miss a shot?" asked Ali.

"Most of the time, yes. To be honest, I don't really know what it is, but when I'm doing something that requires focus like shooting from a distance, my thoughts disappear and I amalgamate into the task at hand. It sounds really strange, I know, but it's a difficult concept to put into words. It's something that you would need to experience to fully understand."

"So do you see my predicament now, young man? You've understood that words can only take you so far."

"But how does this relate to the golden truth that you speak about?"

"The golden truth, and what so many prophets and sages have intended to explain, is that there is a vast reserve of intelligence that lies within you, one that is connected to something immaterial. A sleeping giant, if you will, that awakes when you take no thought... it can either be used to kill, to create, or to make more informed decisions about your life and how to better provide for your family."

"I have never killed anyone," said the guard, quick to correct Ali.

"Good. And so if you really want to do what you love and to be good at it, or to gain the object of your desire, you must be in touch with this power, or higher awareness, within yourself. If you're serious about this, then you must see yourself for what you are... and this is where the more religious and spiritual aspect comes in, because *you* are the Universe experiencing itself – this is a divine revelation, and one must be mindful of this if they are to value anything worthwhile: to be able to live *consciously,* and not by accident."

"Okay, but ..", The guard was interrupted as Ali interjected.

"-Answer me this", he said.

The guard let out an exasperated sigh, "Really? Another detour?"

"*Answer* me this question", Ali insisted. "What do you regard as being the most beautiful thing in the world?"

The guard was beginning to find this tedious. He looked visibly tense at Ali's eccentricity, but immediately replied: "The most beautiful thing in the world is my wife."

"Tell me about your wife."

"My wife?"

"Yes, your wife. How do you feel about her?"

"I feel like we share a secret, just the two of us... the thing where you want to be with one person all the time, and you feel like you both understand something no one else gets. I could just tell her everything about myself... she feels like... home home. Yeah... *home* is the best way to describe her."

"And is that why you love her?"

"I love her because... I just *know* that I love her. I knew from the moment I saw her."

"How do you feel when you see her?"

"When I look at her I feel... peaceful, safe. My mind stops completely."

"Why?"

"Because what else is there to think about? When I look into her eyes, I see everything I want right in front of me. She's just *perfect*... It's like the whole of creation programmed me in a way to admire her and only her. It's as if she was made for me, and that my only obligation in this life is to recognise and appreciate her... everything about her, it's not just one single thing. I could go on, but if I must specify a sole reason for loving her, then I guess you could say it's because of the feeling she gives me."

"What feeling is that?"

"Well, I already said... love, like I am home..."

"What else?"

The guard didn't know what else to say, but his face affirmed a realisation as he began to speak. "...*Certainty*," he confessed, nodding his head in conviction. "I know I love her because she makes me feel... *certain*."

"Certain of your love for her...?"

"Exactly, yes."

"And what does that do to you?"

"It makes me feel powerful, like I have the strongest motivation in the whole world! All I want to do is show her how much I love her. She makes me grateful to be alive. She makes me want to give back... to do something really special with this life.... Ah, wow..." he said in awe, making the mental connection between what he had said, before concluding:

"To be certain about what I find beautiful, is indeed a beautiful thing in itself. It makes me feel that I really know myself... like I have a true purpose."

Ali reclined backwards, revelling in a feeling of quiet satisfaction. "Congratulations, young man. You have described something that no words can describe."

The guard felt proud of his breakthrough, but still persisted, "But, Ali..."

"Yes, yes. You want to know about the ultimate truth?"

"Yes, please."

"So let's say you found the ultimate truth... I want you to imagine what that would do to you" Ali preempted.

"Okay..." the guard closed his eyes, trying to visualise the scenario.

Ali continued, "Is it fair to say that once you have found the *ultimate truth*, you would always know what to say and what to do from that point onwards?"

"I guess so, because I would feel *certain*, right?"

"Exactly, young man. The recognition of beauty; your being certain that something is beautiful, would spark an expression of certainty that leads you directly to what you value, and the choices you make in your life."

The guard studied Ali, fixated, knowing that he was painting a picture with his words.

Ali asked, "Who is recognising the beauty that you recognise in your wife? Is it your mind, your body... or your soul?"

"Everything. Every fibre of my being."

"And unto your very essence..." Ali reinforced, pointing toward his chest.

"Yes."

"And who created your being? Your essence? Who was it that made you in its image, and left its image in your eye?"

The guard stared blankly.

"Know this....Regardless of what happened, or will happen in this world, something loved you enough to give you the gift of life and with it, the curious gift of loving something deeply. Something gave you the power of recognition for beauty, and it is exactly within this power that you will find your answer. The answer is obtained when, through love, one gains the courage to dive into the unknown. Think about it, are you not to worship that essence within you, which is the very source of the love you have for your wife and for your family?"

Still perplexed, the guard glanced at Ali compassionately, wondering now whether these were the ramblings of an old man.

"Learn and gain knowledge not by asking of it, but by experiencing it." Ali continued, "Dive into unseen horizons, but do not ask how to dive. Ready food is eaten easily, so cook your own food yourself. Only then can you learn how a plate of food is prepared. The one who cooks it can appreciate its true taste. Evolving to understand your truth is this."

"Evolving? How does one evolve?"

"Evolving means looking at your mind thoroughly and honestly and seeing all of its tendencies and shortcomings. It's viewing your mind objectively as the silent observer, until the illusions of the outside dissolve in the light of your awareness. Through conscious evolution, you come closer to the embers of the flame of your eternal love, the love that represents the love of the creator in you."

The afternoon sun shone down onto Ali's face. The guard sat, patiently, hanging onto every word, trying his best to comprehend.

"To take care of that which you love is your true purpose," Ali recited, "to discover what you love is to find your purpose. To gain meaning out of life's heartbreak is the ultimate act of rebellion toward a reckless God. There lies the golden line of truth which hangs by a thread, separating the good and bad, the higher and lower, the yin and yang paradoxes of life. For when the sleeping giant awakens within you, he remembers this middle path, knowing exactly what to do, and exactly what to say."

The guard brooded over Ali's cryptic parable, "How...?" he asked.

"Awaken the sleeping giant within you with the light of your awareness. Discover and walk your path, yours and yours alone. You are never lost in your own home."

The guard felt calmed, now accepting the mysterious nature of Ali's cognition. He concentrated on the inflexions in Ali speech, the pregnant pause between sentences, trying to understand the poignancy of his teachings.

"You say I'm angry at God, young man?" Ali directed his question more bluntly, causing the guard to flinch at the sudden change in tone.

"It seems you are... But what did you mean by rebelling against God? By finding meaning?"

Ali carefully scanned his corpus of knowledge to procure the right answer. "Earlier I called your army the army of Satan" he said.

"Yes you did," the guard tried to conceal his irritation.

"But really, after thinking about it, I know now that you are working for the army of God."

The guard was relieved, "What makes you say that?"

"Because if there is one thing I have learnt about God, it's that he loves to destroy that which he creates. He so casually allows the death of that which is regarded as sacred." Once more the guard fell silent, hoping the pinnacle of Ali's narration wouldn't take as long as before. "But I am not angry at God, not anymore. I will not give him the pleasure!" declared Ali.

The guard nodded in agreement, afraid of appearing contrary. He wanted to enquire about Ali's use of masculine pronouns, but decided not to derail the conversation further. He concluded it must be due to an old ingrained habit. "What do you mean you won't 'give him the pleasure'?"

"God wanted my family to die in that war. Nothing happens that is not already written in the plan of the all-*merciful* creator. All events take place under his watch."

"Okay..." the guard waited, timing the sluggish pace of Ali's words.

"He wanted my wife to be crushed under the rubble. He destined my daughter to be shot, he intended for my son to be buried alive..." Ali continued, his words quivering under a wave of sadness. "He knew I would cry his name in vain... all part of his great cosmic plan." Ali stopped, and looked back toward the guard, "But do you know what he doesn't know?"

"Tell me..." the guard shook his head, pitifully aware of Ali's allegorical demeanour.

"That to inflict pain onto me, he had to make me conscious in the first place. He had to make a free spirit, a divine soul born from his conscious eternal flame. A flame that sparks my limitless love for my family, forever until eternity. This is a truth that stands the test of time, a love that remains when tested by any reasoning, subjectivity or objectivity of the material realm. It is this truth that I remain eternally grateful for and which I live for.

For I do not need an eternity with my family to realise the fulfilment of my life. All I could ever ask for was a single day with someone, *something* I loved more than anything in the world. I reject wordy meanings and philosophy, for it is in my power and mine alone to remain in the gratitude of this simple truth. The gratitude of simply being alive as a conscious, self-aware piece of the cosmos, and to recognise the universal miracle of a single, true, loving moment. In recognising this truth, no matter what fate beckons me ahead, it is my duty to remain in this gratitude as I pass from this life onto the next."

The guard was captured by the emotions of Ali's words rather than the words themselves. He intuitively replied, "I can't imagine the pain you must be reliving on a daily basis..."

"All I ever needed was a single moment with my family... a single second of the eternal truth of my love. For in a desolate Universe, what more can one ask for? This is your golden line of truth, young man, a precious element that does not erode in the dirt. The invincible objectivity; a truth that nobody can take from you, not even God. *This* is the ultimate act of rebellion toward a careless God, who turns the wheel of life and death. It is to hold on to that eternal gratitude of that which you love, and to let go of all else that weakens your grip. It is to inquire into the *source* of this love, and find your undeniable power inside.

Awaken to your rights young man. Awaken to that which no book can ever record, no sage can ever teach. For your own heart is your ultimate religion, breath is your ultimate prayer, and consciousness is your ultimate God.

Know this, young man, and find this truth for yourself. You can never be lost in your own home."

The guard turned toward the light emanating from the window, "I understand now."

"This is the ultimate purpose of the awakened man." Ali lectured on, "It is to find something you care about so deeply that you would calmly face death to protect it. It is knowing that whatever happens, you will always be eternally grateful for that *moment* where you experienced the certainty of truth; of love, and all of which you cared about. It is to live in that truth until your inevitable death, and nothing can take that away from you, not even God – no matter how hard he tries."

"And how do I find that thing? Well, apart from my family?"

"By having the courage and patience to sit with yourself in solitude. To observe your thoughts, until they realise that you can hear them, but not in the way they wished. As you become the authoritarian parent of your mind, your thoughts eventually relent, quieting down like sobered children. And when the mind is silent, your heart may finally be heard. It may take you ten seconds, and on other days it may take hours. You must sit with yourself until your mind becomes completely naked."

"No clothes... like a virgin consciousness," the guard blurted.

"Precisely, young man. It's the ability to view yourself from the sexy vantage point of ultimate reality, free of the fog that clouds your essence, until..."

"...until you know what you *love*... until you always know what to do... and you always know what to say."

"Absolutely correct, my friend."

"I see!... ah... I see.. I see." the guard repeated, nodding in realisation. "Now I understand why you took me on that journey."

"The ultimate paradox, young man. The simplest truth, yet the most difficult to comprehend."

"And that's why the world needs people like you!"

"The world just needs the right student. Soon you will devise new ways to improve my teachings."

"Oh...I doubt that. But I accept the compliment."

"Well, I don't doubt it at all," Ali's face beamed with a warm smile.

The guard, noticing Ali's contentment, settled on his own contemplation, grinning at the satiating conversation they had shared.

"I love my wife so much," said the guard out loud.

"What's her name?"

"Eve."

"...really?"

"No, I'm kidding, her name is Chloe"

"Chloe... what a beautiful name" Ali nodded in admiration, letting the conclusive comment consume the silence, as they stopped to reflect. Nobody ever felt more comfortable in that prison cell.

The silence eventually broke with the sound of Ali overreaching to retrieve some ruffled papers. However, the shackles restricted his movement, making it hard for him to manoeuvre.

"What are you doing?" the guard asked.

"I keep my favourite translations to myself", he said, unfolding one of the papers and placing the rest back underneath him.

"Oh... I guess that's why my superiors ask me if I've checked your cell each day... I've never seen those papers before... Were you hiding them? Nevermind, which one is your favourite?"

"Take a guess" Ali replied, holding the paper as he gazed over it proudly.

"A Zoroastrian text?"

"Good guess," Ali smiled. "Here, I want you to have it... you won't tell anyone, will you?"

"Don't be silly," said the guard, grabbing the text enthusiastically.

"Keep that one safe, it will help you with your writing."

"Thank you, I will... I will. Ah, really, thanks so much."

"And have you got something for me?"

"What?... Oh, you mean the contract?"

"Yes, I promised I would keep my word," a hint of resignation in Ali's voice.

The guard had become so engrossed in the conversation, he completely forgot about the contract and his duty to coerce Ali to sign. "Here you go," he said, as he handed him the paper and pen.

Ali signed the paper without reading it. Apathetic and disinterested in its contents, he dropped the paper, fell with his back against the wall. He let out a long sigh, and rolled the pen over to the guard.

"Are you okay?" Ali's complexion was pale and the guard was concerned.

"I'm fine," Ali whimpered dismissively. "Do you feel better now?"

"About the contract? Yes... I was under increasing pressure to get you to sign. They were asking me to hurry."

"Pressure... I forget what that feels like. Never be in a hurry, young man. Do everything quietly and in a calm spirit. Do not lose your inner peace for anything whatsoever, even if your whole world seems out of alignment."

The afternoon air felt a little lighter, but the sound of Ali's laboured breath alerted the guard to the gravity of the situation.

"Wait here, I'm going to get some medical attention." He said with urgency. "You don't have to sit here like this anymore."

"Sit back down here!" Ali demanded. "Please. Stay with me for a little longer, I'm not done with you yet."

"But, Ali, I-"

"Sit down, *please*." Ali insisted.

The guard reluctantly lumbered back down.

"Read that paper to me," Ali asked, "it's Zoroaster's teaching in his own words, written over two thousand six hundred years ago."

"Okay... of course, Ali," the guard agreed reluctantly. He was more concerned about Ali's declining health.

He straightened the page and cleared his throat. "Ahem... or should I say 'Amen.' And so Zoroaster once said..."

"Louder, young man"

"AND SO ZOROASTER ONCE SAID:

THERE IS NOTHING FOR YOU OUTSIDE.

REALISE YOU ARE FROM GOOD SPIRIT, MADE OF GOOD SPIRIT, AND WILL RETURN TO GOOD SPIRIT. YOU ARE GOD'S PERFECT THOUGHT, LIVING IN GOD'S IDEA; PERFECTION.

LOOK INWARD TO THE GOD MIND AND SEE TRUTH, AND EXPERIENCE SOUNDNESS OF MIND.

THOUGHTS MAKE YOUR WORLD, BELIEFS MAKE YOUR THOUGHTS, REASON MAKES YOUR BELIEFS. MIND REASONS, MIND IS THE REASON.

KNOW THIS, THE ILLUSION GOES AWAY."

The guard looked up at Ali and smiled before he continued:

"AWAKEN TO WHO YOU ARE.

THINK GOOD [GOD] THOUGHTS, NOT EVIL [DEVIL] THOUGHTS,

SAY GOOD WORDS,

DO GOOD DEEDS.

LIVING IN TRUTH IS LIFE WITHOUT ENEMIES, FOR IN TRUTH THE EVIL, THE LIE AND ILLUSION IS RENDERED NOTHING.

SO GO ADAM, IN TRUTH, AND ENJOY THIS WONDERFUL LIFE!"

"Wait, so is God talking about the same Adam, from Adam and Eve?" the guard asked.

"'Adam' is the word for 'human' or 'man' in Persian. But I translated it like that to put your name in there for fun. I saved that one for you to remember."

"How did you know my name?"

"I speak many languages."

"What else happened in the story of Adam and Eve?"

"That is a story for another time, Adam. May you remove my shackles now?" Ali stretched his arms outright, poised in position.

"Yes, of course, sorry. I almost forgot." Adam hurriedly took the keys from his belt to unlock Ali's hands. "I'm so sorry, Ali..." his head bowed in remorse.

"It's not your fault."

"So, shall we go, then?"

"Go where?"

"To the Ministry, of course! They've been expecting you for quite a while."

"Oh, I see... I was just beginning to get comfortable here."

"Please Ali, there's no need for you to be here anymore. Let's go." Adam was insistent. He crouched down to help scoop Ali off the floor.

"Look, young man." For reasons unbeknown, Ali was quite content. "You'll have to excuse me for my quirkiness, but I think I'd like to stay here another night."

"What?! Are you crazy? You mean you're not coming?!"

"I know it sounds strange, but there is something quite desirable about staying here one more night without those shackles. Just me, alone with my thoughts... knowing that I'm now a free man. I would just like one more night. Besides, you can tell them I signed the contract in the morning."

"Are you sure about this Ali? Is this another one of your jokes?" Adam was baffled.

"No jokes. Not this time. I'm just feeling a little... *sentimental*, that's all."

Adam was mystified. "Well, can I at least get you a pillow, or something?"

"No, thank you. This is perfect."

"Okay... well, I guess, let me know if you need anything?" replied Adam. He slowly exited, closing the cell door gently behind him. This time leaving it slightly ajar, making a point not to lock it. As he began to walk away, he suddenly called out, "Oh, and Ali... I'm going to try that meditation tonight. How should I do it again?"

"Well, there are many ways... but for you?" Ali paused, running his fingers across the metal marks on his wrists and forearms. "As you go about your day, simply remind yourself to repeat the words, 'I am' in your head, as many times as you can."

"I am?"

"Yes, 'I am'. And say it out loud, if you can."

"That's it?"

"That's it."

"*I am…*" the guard whispered. He had a look of bemusement as he stared at the floor.

"Oh, and Adam…"

"Yes, Ali?"

"Leave this place when you can. Take your aim toward your writing instead, you have a great story to tell. The world needs your perspective."

"I will, thank you… I will," the guard beamed with gratification.

"And Adam…"

"Yes, Ali?"

"Listen to your wife. She is the single biggest career decision you will make."

"I will Ali, I promise."

"Good night, young man."

"Good night, Ali…

Thank you, Ali."

CHAPTER

7

Ali didn't recall falling asleep. He must have dozed off unsuspectingly, and woke up feeling slightly delirious. What an eventful day it had been. As he lay staring at the ceiling, he noticed a feeling of liberation around his indentured wrists, his skin stained black from where his shackles once restrained him. He realised that he could now simply stand up and walk out of the cell, something that seemed impossible only a few hours ago. But alas, in a state of indifference, he rested one last time on the cell floor, feeling a mix of disdain and ambivalence for the fate that awaited him on the outside. He drew an exhausted breath, as he recounted the events that had unfolded that day.

On a more positive note, he noticed that he had successfully managed to gain some degree of mastery over his own internal world, and this was something that he valued very dearly. He often wrote books on man's ability to overcome the chains of his past, on how to live more consciously and empowered. Ali realised that the shackles now laid out before him were a metaphor for his memories; negative and disempowering thoughts that clung to him like a dead weight. He saw them now as attachments that had deceived him, tricking him into thinking they belonged to him.

He noticed a certain looseness, something new that he hadn't experienced in a while. He wondered if it was due to the cell door being open, even though he had no intention to walk outside. Or maybe it was a result of him meditating, even though he had only just started two nights ago. Or, perhaps it was the conversation with the prison guard, "Adam..." he said, smiling to himself. His honest self-reflection had unleashed a source of newfound optimism. For after countless years of stagnation, he once again felt the enchanting satisfaction that one gets after accomplishing a meaningful task.

He was tempted to indulge in these fresh ideas, now eagerly erupting in his mind, but he knew the most valuable of insights would eventually reveal themselves through the mysterious sound of silence. With these things in mind, Ali settled one last time into a quiet mode of contemplation. He reminded himself that there was nothing for him to do, nobody that he needed to be, and nothing he needed to say. Our lonesome prisoner sat with his back up against the wall and his hands by his lap. He closed his eyes and sunk into the void of his awareness, watching nature do its magic.

His eyes were closed for just a moment, when he noticed his vision becoming suspiciously bright and argent. Sensing an acute, visceral presence in front of him as though being watched, he asked "Can I not have one night to myself?"

"You've had enough time to yourself, don't you think?..
What are you doing still sitting here? Did not your idol
Zoroaster denounce indolent behaviour?"

The voice was different; deep and commanding, yet endearing.

Ali carefully opened his eyes to be confronted by a glowing
figure of grandeur. He saw a sword-wielding male that
emanated a reflective silver, dressed in wondrous colours.
Almost accustomed to these celestial visitations, Ali felt more
at ease this time, almost privileged to be granted counsel
with such supremacy.

"Who are you, the guard's uncle?" joked Ali.

"I'm glad to see you still have your sense of humour. A
telling sign of strength," the luminous being was pleased.

"Who are you?"

"I am that generous consolation that arrives for every old
man. The prayers you whispered at the gates of an ineffectual
heaven were finally heard. So, it was only a matter of time
before I came down to pay you a visit, and offer some words
of solace to calm your aching, dying mind."

"I see you've been listening to my previous conversations...
How do you know I'm dying?" asked Ali.

"Because *you* know you are dying."

Ali was deflated, "Is this it, then? Is this the answer to my prayers? Is this how I am rewarded for my pious years of devotion to my faith? To die in this cell?"

"Well Ali, what would the Islamic scholars say? Shall we choose an Indian Sufi, Hazrat Inayat Khan: '*I asked for strength, and God gave me difficulties to make me strong. I asked for wisdom, and God gave me problems to learn to solve. I asked for prosperity, and God gave me a brain and brawn to work. I asked for courage, and God gave me dangers to overcome. I asked for love, and God gave me people to help. I asked for favours, and God gave me opportunities. I received nothing I wanted...*'"

"...and I received everything I needed." Ali concluded in unison.

"Correct, Ali, for only in pain did you find your will, and only in your chaos did you learn to be still. Only in your fear did you find your might, and only in darkness do you recognise your light."

"Well.. I don't think I've found my might."

"And what is might to you?"

"To be mighty, to carry a sword like yours... to wield the enthusiasm of that youthful guard... but I cannot soldier on, there is no strength left in an old man like me," retorted

Ali. "And if you are here to offer me some advice on my newfound adventure, please, do not waste your breath... I only signed that paper to appease the burdens of that poor young man. I have no intention of butting heads and twisting arms to overthrow an entire army."

"But Ali, don't you see?" the warrior being lifted his sword like a feather and pointed at it while grinning, "You have mastered a weapon much mightier than this one."

"I don't understand. How?"

"How?!" the figure bellowed in compassionate amusement:

"Because you are a Navy Seal, Ali! You chart the oceans of thought; your principles sink like anchors, deep below the surface of the minds of men.

You are a Paratrooper; your words float over the judgement of the ignorant, your points landing silently in the base of their conscience.

You are a Commandeer; your recruits armed with your vigorous contours of discourse, rescuing truths from ill-intentioned terrain.

You are a Samurai; your blade sharpened on the stone of your conscience.

My wordsmith Ali, who wields a sword of truth with double-edged meanings, who ruptures sheilds of injustice with his carefully weighted words. Oh truthful Ali, you are here to inform men, not fight them.

That is why no unworthy institution shall capture your cognition, not under my watch."

"Ah, I see... very poetic," Ali was half-impressed.

"And while your intellect delivers your marching orders and your heart conjures the dreams of the innocent" the being continued, "it is *my* conviction that delivers your call to action" he concluded, piercing the stone floor with his shining sword.

"Who... are you?"

"*I am the voice in your gut*, and I shall never allow you to work in the belly of the beast."

"You... are the voice in my gut?..."

"Know this, Ali, your gut is a gasoline tank, your mind is an engine, its pistons explode through the dynamism of your heart. So they call me the fire in your belly. *I am* the instinct that gives you the conviction to know when to throw away all taboo and when to cast aside all teachings, all judgement, and when to trust that gleam of light that flashes across your mind from within."

"So... it was *you* who told me it didn't feel right... But, why? Logically, their proposition seemed to make sense. Why did you not let me accept my freedom? What is your reasoning?"

"Because the road to hell is often paved with good intentions. These elite institutions, intelligence agencies being no exception, have become so perfectly constructed that anyone who enters them and immerses themselves in them, inevitably, will become co-opted by them. No matter how well-intentioned you are, no matter how resistant you think you are to their pieties, you will never gain the influence required to make meaningful change. The reward systems for such *intelligent* agents have been so perfected to work in the favour of the beast. Every mission you are set, each task required of you operates through moral compromise, ingraining you more and more into the system each day, until you no longer realise what is a compromise and what is not. This is no worthy adventure for a warrior of truth."

"Then... what is the purpose of your being here, if not to convince me to work for them?"

"I am here because Salma sent me to guide you."

"That's... impossible," Ali replied, "my wife... only exists in my dreams."

"And dreams serve to reflect that which you hold alive in your heart."

"My heart belongs to her... but since she left, it seems I have felt so unsure, so lost for all these years."

"You have experienced a tsunami of trauma, Ali. Trauma causes a disturbance in any man's ability to trust in his instinctual abilities. But doubt not, you have done well, do not be so hard on yourself. You were willing to die for something, and this was the saving grace that pushed you to the core of your heart's pain, and with it, the source of your wisdom."

Ali stroked his beard in his habitual manner, indulging in the fiery validation of this blazing figure. Above all, he finally felt understood, "So then... what has trauma done to my mind?"

"Trauma has caused you to become suspicious & untrusting, negative and pessimistic, addictive, self-sabotaging, scattered and distracted, demotivated and drained of energy, self-deprecating, judgmental of yourself and others, emotionally cut off-"

"Okay, okay..." Ali interrupted, "I'm sorry I asked." He caught his reflection in the sword, etched in insecurity.

"But you have to know the truth, Ali! And any man with the courage to sit alone with his thoughts deserves it. For while the mind can terrify you, know that fear is but a tool of the man-made devil. There is beauty to be found in the darkest of places... especially in the darkest of places. Confront the truth so that you can overcome it, there lies your power."

"I see..." muttered Ali, accepting the weight of the warrior's burdensome words.

"You do see, Ali.. men see that they love the truth, but many desire welcome truths, and reject those that are unwelcome. Men are often afraid of that which they do not know, and, not knowing the truth, they are afraid to receive it. That is why you must learn to love your unwelcome truths, and do not fear them. After all, we are God's co-workers, not slaves, and to carry the will of the creator is to fear no evil."

"Yes, yes I know. I wrote about this... I'm starting to remember... But with all due respect, why are you here to tell me all of this *now*?"

"I came to offer words of deprogramming. Just like the voice in your head and heart."

"Deprogramming? What do you mean?"

"There are programs in your mind that have been written by an array of traumatising experiences. While those experiences were destined for you, your nervous system has been struggling to process them. Through no fault of your own, you have not fully unravelled the knots of wisdom gained from your journey. Instead, they remain lodged in your gut like little gallstones of sadness. These unprocessed emotions are causing doubt in you; doubt in your own abilities i.e. your writing. This is problematic for the reason of what I am about to ask you."

"Ah, right... I thought maybe you were here to protect me against evil, or something."

"The most ardent shield against evil is to be at peace with yourself, for the true enemy of the devil is contentment."

"Okay, so you're here to make me content. Well, that is very kind. Obviously I have no say in the matter, so just tell me what I need to do," Ali said, subdued and cooperative.

The warrior-like being put his sword to one side, stepped forward, and slowly knelt down on one knee. He looked at Ali admiringly, with a relaxed smile in his eyes. He put one hand of camaraderie on his shoulder. Ali felt a warm, uplifting vibration travel up his spine, around his shoulders and down toward his hands. "I know what you are going through," he told Ali, "allow your feelings to surface." Ali sat with his back against the wall, his eyes watering at the intensity of the experience.

"Face everything that is there, Ali. Relax with it. Do not be afraid of your own mind."

Ali could hardly let out any words, "Alright..." he whispered.

"Remember what you used to write, Ali - about the mind. What was the main teaching?"

Ali thought for a moment, "I... can't remember," he said, feeling utterly depleted.

"Your main teaching is that *you are not your mind*... does that sound about right, Ali?"

"Yes... that was it."

"And what was your famous rhyme: '*Remain with the observing spark...*'?"

"*...Remain with the observing spark... that lights and dissolves all that seems dark*" Ali recollected.

"That's a wonderful saying, isn't it?"

Ali struggled to reply. He let out a defeated sigh before masking his emotions with a small cough. "Yes... it is," he said, "it's a nice saying."

"And why?" the being continued, smiling endearingly toward Ali, "Because once a man has remained true to strengthening his light for an epoch, it becomes his responsibility to share his light with whomever crosses his path, be they a friend or an *enemy*." He reached over to place a comforting hand on Ali's cheek, "You've done well, young man. You have done this world a world of good," he said, nodding, "you know that, right?"

With that proclamation began a physiological change in Ali's chemistry; a wave of exultation slowly lifted his spirit in a way he had never felt before. His mind began to clear itself of the state lethargy into which it had lapsed. His faculty of reason began to work once more. "I know why you are here..." he said, "I know what has happened." He turned to one side and stared into the cold air in amazement.

"Ha, very good," the being said, pleased as he stood back up and reached for his sword. He placed it vertically in front of him again, leaning on it jovially and asked, "what have you realised?"

"I was never meant to continue my life in an audacious attempt to sabotage the enemy's operations... No, the guard's name... Adam... his wife... his stories are so similar to mine... chosen to watch over me for his competency, but really, he is very young, why not choose someone more experienced? Why the same guard for all these years?"

"A coincidence, perhaps?" the warrior smugly replied.

"No... it was destined for us to meet... the dream I had... the beings who came at night, they were aligning our union. It was a presage for me to engage with him. Is that the true purpose of why I'm here, in this prison cell?"

"Ah, *purpose*... that's a funny little word" the figure replied, his smile growing "Why such a surprise? The Universe isn't interested in your achievements... just your heart. When you choose to act out of compassion, you are already harmonised with your true purpose. No need to look any further!"

"But... all this talk of fearlessness, of following your path, strong and resolute..."

"What is strength to you, Ali? Brunt and brawn? What about the strength to forgive, and the strength to see oneself honestly? What about the endurance of patience, and the persistence of encouragement? Your immense sensitivity makes you a warrior servant of humanity. Your vulnerability breeds equitable treatment and fulfilment of mercy. This offers a greater purpose in the world, more than any sternness ever will."

The figure's gleaming, expectant eyes pierced deep into Ali's core. Ali remained stunned in quietude as he looked around him, thinking intensely, his expression revealed a realisation that struck him:

"My sickness... my shame, my anger, my guilt... was from myself, but I did not perceive it. The remedy for evil was within me, but I did not sense it..."

"You were bound to evil because of your hate for evil, and in hating evil you loved it secretly, for you love to hate it." the being explained.

"I loved to hate evil..."

"This bred an invisible pride, trapping you into guilt; your shame, no matter how innocent it seemed on the surface. For only the humble forgive themselves, and only the prideful remain in their perfectionism. Accepting evil is what frees you from your predicament. As you began to accept those unlovable parts of yourself, you released the Devil's grip from your fate. Anchored in principle, the warrior of truth brings forth goodness, he is not swept away by what he does not want. Knowing thy enemy, he recognises evil's share in life, and in doing so, he deprives it of the power it has to overwhelm him."

"I just... I had no need to look beyond the small confines of this cell. What I sought was within me, if only I would reflect. If only I let go of my guilt... if only I let go of my pride."

"This is why the simple act of letting go is the noblest triumph a man can accomplish. He gives back to the world by taking care of himself. He places no resistance on the love emanating from the fountain of his soul. In doing so, he spills over that which the world needs above all. As for your teachings, you can only attempt to perceive the impact you have had on this world - in places you least expected. For all it takes is to teach one person who is willing to learn. All it takes is *one* conversation that will irrevocably change the course of a man's life. Unto the course of history, and to worlds beyond! This is how you save the world, not by status or military position."

Ali felt a rush of emotion charge through his body. He attempted to stand up straight for the first time in a long while, but immediately, his weak knees buckled as he tried to leap upwards. Gravity ungraciously pulled him back to the floor. Dismayed and disillusioned, he cried out towards the valiant figure "I must go on."

"Your work here is done, Ali."

"But I have not worked as much as I could, I still have some fight left in me!"

"You have worked quite enough. Rest here now."

"No, I denounce idleness." Ali was insistent, attempting in vain to stand up once more.

"Then pick up your pen from the floor, translate the remaining texts until you can read no more. Then, you must write your penultimate piece of work."

"Write? About what?"

"Certainty."

"Certainty?"

"Yes, the certainty gained from strengthening one's inner light. Write about the wonders of this inner light, paint the process of this strengthening. Compose, for your reader, the symphony of the certain, ideal character; the awakened archetype, the man who navigates through this world of half-truths."

"I see... well, I can... paint a picture, I guess... So, is this it? asked Ali, "I've finally fallen, never to face the world again?"

"Not quite. The warrior who falls in battle is never considered fallen, for his ideals stand, nonetheless. He earns preferential treatment from death, and laughs with his Lord as they meet in the world thereafter."

Ali reached over and picked up his pen and the first two papers, scanning them intently with his trained eyes and his multilingual mind. "God's sick game," he mumbled, "I didn't know he was *laughing*."

"Of course, God is laughing all the time! And so your humility magnetises you to his strength!" The voice of the radiant warrior, calm yet unleashed, shuddered through the stone walls, "And when we are free from ourselves, we realize that we are hearing our own laughter. Why? Because all of the fear and the sadness of the ego is itself a cosmic joke. For the punchline is that we fear nothing, because we are nothing at that level of the dream. We are everything and simultaneously the source of everything. We do not die, and we were never really born. We are the clandestine masters of this whole dream.

In forgetting this, our consciousness falls victim to forces that we eventually must redeem. And when you have realised your freedom, what greater realisation is there? The joy of realizing the perfection of it all; that the whole Universe is a beautiful work of art in an astronomical theatre of dreams.

Soon you will discover that all of time is present in the eternal now, and the beauty of the world is all but a flower in the Lord's garden, and as the gardener of this beautiful flower, you shall birth a new flower on the tree of life. A new world, with even greater beauty than you could ever imagine. It shall engulf you with great joy, peace and creative energy like never before.

So indeed my friend, laughter and humour; living the pantomime and being the cosmic joke are an essential process in the evolution of man. Thus he marches on, unsullied by circumstance, rising in consciousness to ever-higher echelons, until he can hear God reciting the joke as it happens, whilst knowing the punchline ahead of time. In this knowing, he savours each moment of this life, smiling at the arrival of death.

As for you, my humble Ali, nomadic traveller of time, student of the middle way, there is no beginning, middle or end to your eternal story. For today you write the pages that turn the minds of man toward their final chapters, and tomorrow you leave the earth behind, climb the etheric terraces and peer into the unknown, searching for the portals of a faraway celestial city.

May you learn and grow forevermore, with certainty your tool.

So it is written:

> *Here lies the story of Ali;*
>
> *dearly beloved friend of the truth.*
>
> *Our mighty hero,*
>
> *and our wonderful fool."*

CHAPTER

8

So, we began this story with the predicament of Ali. It seems he was rewarded with a valuable insight, from a precious debt that truth owed him. In the darkest of places, Ali discovered that as long as he remained truthful, he would be helped; guided, to receive all the wisdom his heart desired. In the realisation that all good deeds are returned, Ali became aware of the unspoken. Namely, that truth is neither a word or doctrine; nor does it belong to a system or a school. But as the ancients before us have realized, truth is a living organism. It is a creature in itself; independent with its own life and death, its own beginning and ending, with infinitude beyond our comprehension. Ali learnt that truth was a great teacher. His main lesson? To grasp that truth alone could lead a man to perfection. Thus, Ali gained his perfection by selflessly giving his own life to truth.

In this way, we are able to understand how the ancients of the old fathomed the mysteries of life. We think of things today merely as objects. We regard *hope* singularly as a word representing an emotion. We think of wisdom merely as mental penetration. We think of love as a duality of personal emotion, but simultaneously an emotion shared by others. To the ancients, however, these so-called feelings were actually *beings*.

Love was a reality; love was a creature, not just a relationship. And from all the ancient and classical writings, we find that the Greeks, Indians, Egyptians and Persians - and typically all foreign peoples, have personified their virtues. When they think of strength, they think of a particular power, when they think of wisdom, they think of a person who is wise. The ancients created Gods for every emotion, thought and attitude of the human mind. Hope was another *being*, something that grew like a child in its mother's womb. Hope was a great moment of spent veneration, like the individual taking holy orders. These represented personifications or embodiments of principles that appear to us as a language of symbolism; a language that enables us to share in the wisdom which they impact.

Ali saw from his first radiant apparition a vision of enlightened love, realising that she had been with him from the beginning. And from the moment he dedicated his life to truth, she was with him and would remain with him until the end of his days. How and why? Because no truthful man walks through life entirely alone, and those who give themselves to unselfish service to others are rewarded with a radiant presence that will remain beside them as they truly deserve it. They will inextricably be with something, someone, somewhere who is ever and always waiting to help, to use this truth that they have discovered in order to save them further punishment, suffering and pain. They have earned the peace of inner life, and will behold it regardless of what happens in the outer world.

And so, the wisdom that Ali had assembled to teach others was now taught to him. It was shown to him conclusively that his dreams had not been fables, that his ideas had not been vacuums created by optimism or pessimism and that, in reality, the truth is alive and walks with those who serve it.

Regardless of how we view the matter, it is a beautiful thought, a very kindly thought. And it was this thought that gave consolation to our lonely prisoner who was condemned to die alone. This brings us very definitely to the concept of truth as love, as the most dynamic way that leads to reality. Therefore, it was quite apt for these ancients to think of love as the faithful friend; something that could dissolve beyond all of the troubles of the mind. For the mind can be deceived; the body can be punished, but the truth in the soul is everlasting, and once set in motion, nothing can curtail it. So, when the time came, Ali passed on without fear, doubt or loneliness.

There is no question that much of this is symbolic, but nonetheless, it's something that our ancestors have given great deal of thought to, perhaps for good reason. It is only in our modern scientific world that we transform these beings into scientific formulae of numbers and letters as a means of interpreting the orchestrations of atoms. Really, the answers to all the riddles of knowledge; the source of energies, the nature of light and darkness, of good and evil, are all formulas of a vibratory rate, and they are all alive. Everything contains life; from a stone; to a star; together intertwined by a tremendous unity. Some of the great physicists of the past century have touched upon this wonder:

"As a man who has devoted his whole life to the most clear-headed science, to the study of matter, I can tell you as a result of my research about atoms this much: there is no matter as such. All matter originates and exists only by virtue of a force which brings the particle of an atom to vibration and holds this most minute solar system of the atom together. We must assume behind this force the existence of a conscious and intelligent mind. This mind is the matrix of all matter." – Max Planck

It also states in Zoroastrian scriptures:

"This worldly existence which is visible and tangible is produced and has arisen from a spiritual existence which is invisible and intangible. In like manner, the lapsing from visibility and tangibility into invisibility and intangibility, are themselves an unquestionable spiritual state." - Sikand-Gumani-Vajar

So Ali went forth to die perfectly content, realizing that he lived in a conscious world in which he not only helped to improve, but would continue to serve him, love him and care for him.

In this way, Ali attained his own vision of an inevitable victory of good over evil. The vision of the victory of faith over fear, of virtue over vice. This vision he attained because nothing can prevent an individual from attaining truth except his own reluctance to improve his ways. It may take a lifetime to acquire perfection in the same way as the conceptual father in heaven is perfect, but the individual must move forward, step by step, in a dedicated search for reality. For the moment he makes the decision to direct and vitalize his own integrity, his journey to the ultimate reality begins.

It is in this moment where the radiant, shining, being of truth takes his hand to lead him to eternity. It is in this moment where the angel comes and says: you have served all your life, you have been a good person, and you are not going to be deserted in your silver hairs, and that the good you have done to others, in fact, is a luminous being, to lead you to the peace and security that you deserve... Under these conditions, this wisdom represents the agency responsible for the unfoldment of human potential to embody our own idea of perfection. Nothing can interrupt it; nothing can prevent the inevitable victory of reality over the illusion.

Until then, man will carry the weight of eternity that ever haunts him in the form of his conscience. Thus, conscience is the territory where all the angelic and demonic entities of human experiences, of virtue and vice, reside, and their influence affects the character of an individual. The sages of our ancestors throughout many cultures acquired a connection to intimately communicate with human consciousness in the form of mystery teachings.

Just like a child that learns the language of his environment as his mental faculties grow over time, the unravelling of mysteries to consciousness is similarly a natural process, if not inhibited by external disturbances. Such external disturbances may include the conflicts of perception such as the use of many languages in the immediate environment of the child. For instance, if the father speaks Italian and the mother speaks French whilst the countrymen are English, then the acumen of that child is challenged, leading to reticent and confusing behaviours. Therefore, the mystery teachings of the ancient sages tend to communicate to these bewildered and perplexed children of mankind. Understanding the principles of their mind would help them become aware of their great, universally-noble potentials.

A Zen teacher once said, *"Before enlightenment; chop wood, carry water. After enlightenment; chop wood, carry water"* - *Zen Kōan*, thereby suggesting that the purpose of man is not to procure a permanent state of pleasure in his enlightenment. Really, the purpose of man is to transform the pains of ignorance in fulfilling the traditions of people, to the pain of wisdom and conscience in fulfilling the divinity in himself.

This takes us to the story of Ali's favourite scholar, Hazrat Inayat Khan, whose father is said to have taught him *"The Prophet [pbuh] has said that God is closer to you than the jugular vein, which in reality means that your own body is farther from you than God is. If this be rightly interpreted, it will mean that God is the very depth of your own being."* This moment was a very great initiation to the young Inayat, as if a switch had turned on in him. He became engaged by this one great truth, witnessing a new life from what he knew and believed. With these things in mind, I leave you with a Jungian teaching that mirrors this replenishing and symbolic truth:

"What good is it to me if this eternal birth of the divine Son takes Place unceasingly, but does not take place within myself? And, what good is it to me if Mary is full of grace if I am not also full of grace? What good is it to me for the

Creator to give birth to his Son if I do not also give birth to him in my time and my culture? This is the fullness of time: When the Son of Man is Begotten in us" - Carl Jung

After all, it was Ali who taught me to keep an open mind, to seek and listen to all authors. Ali taught me to consider the most enlightened thoughts, to choose my own path for myself; the path that led me to write this book in his name and share his story. For it was me whom he helped in that prison cell. While I was sent to guard him, it was Ali who protected me from the most terrifying parts of my mind.

I was that mute companion, destined to bring his papers each morning, along with a meagre breakfast, which I painstakingly attempted to improve. I owe my inspiration to Ali, and as I made him a promise to continue my writing, so I wrote this book as the first of many more. I wished that Ali was here so that I could show him, perhaps he could comment on the many errors in the changes of tones and styles in my writing. Or maybe he would have given me ideas to add more descriptive text to illustrate the beings that came in his cell, although I couldn't see them.

However, I do think that I would have been anxious to show him my work for, little did he know, I was instructed to record my encounters with him, a task of compromise that ate away at me until I stole the recordings and kept the good parts to myself.

Why? Because the world needs to know of Ali, the world needs to see a comprehensive man; someone who's strong but sensitive, someone who's courageous but compassionate. Someone who lives freely from the good in his heart, and doesn't allow his fears to stop him from being true to himself.

Ali gave himself up to whatever the moment brought him, and to whatever question I had for him. I wondered why I so aptly listened to the words of a dying man. To this day, I wonder what would have happened if I had just gone against his advice and sent him the medical help he so stubbornly refused. He rejected my efforts even though he knew that he was going to die, but it was my responsibility to follow my inclination to keep him safe, and alive.

It's my fault for being hypnotised by him, but there was just something about his presence, something that I still can't describe. It was the way he spoke, it was the words he chose when had nothing left to hold on to: no illusions in his mind, no resistances in his body. He had the certainty of a dead man, and his voice put me in a trance. He did not think about his words; they flowed from the core of his being, they carried so much life that... I had no idea he was whispering with death.

Really, he held nothing back from life; therefore he seemed ready for death, as a man is ready for sleep after a good day's work.

But although he seemed ready, I was not. Now, not a single day goes by where I do not wonder what would have happened, how his life could have continued if I just listened to my gut. Now, I have no choice but to be as strong as he was. I have no choice but to be the best I can be, to speak my truth, to try my best, and to do for others what Ali did for me.

Ali, if you are reading this from the distant lands, rest assured that your legacy continues through me. It is evident that you were sent as my catalyst for change, the mirror to illuminate my indiscretions, the accelerant to foster my inspiration. When you departed, as did I. No longer could I condone the abhorrent regime of the army, so I disengaged. As an ode to you, I embarked on a journey for truth. A resonance that even my colleagues could not deny, as a mighty apostasy spilled from within the ranks. Despite the circumstances that threw us together, I tried my utmost to preserve your free will. Painstakingly, I offered what little gestures of liberty I could. But was it enough I ask? I think not.

My penance for caging the mighty eagle, is now to live by your pen. So I write the following chapters in an attempt to convey your wisdom through the lens of my generation. For as long as I continue to face a new day, the world shall not know your end.

Thank you, Ali.

My long lost friend.

CHAPTER

9

Really, if I think about it, I was wrong to call Ali a philosopher. Philosophy is the mediation through language and mathematics, but mostly language. Ali, on the other hand, was more focused on the implication of the present moment. He pointed toward that which is unspoken; the here and now that is silence. Ali encouraged me to focus on an immediacy that would take me out of the linear process of time, which you could say, is mathematical, predictable; outside of the goal of understanding and description of the material plane.

I think therefore that Ali was more of a metaphysician, concerned more with abstract concepts of "being" and "knowing". This is reminiscent of the Bahá'í faith, incidentally another Persian religion (and no, Ali isn't Persian). Like the Bahá'ís, or the Zoroastrians, or the gnostic Christians, or the Islamic mystics, or the Zen monks - the list goes on - Ali wanted me to think about *who* it is that is aware of the material plane, rather than the material plane itself.

For Ali, this *who* is consciousness, or awareness, or you could say scientifically a "zero-point".

Regardless of what we call it, it is something that cannot be spoken of; something without a concept at all. Ali believed that we have the essence of the creator in our essence, making us creators ourselves.

His work also pointed to this world being a kind of spiritual school, created to train, or evolve, our capacity to get in touch with our essence, even through all our material hardships. This was in order to progress a certain spiritual purpose of the cosmos. He viewed life as a conscious teacher aimed at guiding toward this truth. As such, he believed that if one rejects a particular part of themselves, then that rejected part is destined to come back to them in the form of evil, chaos or failure. He pointed, in a way, to the simple teaching that if we do not fix a problem at its source, then it will come back to haunt us again and again, until we learn to transcend it. He observed this to be the main cause of the tyrannical and unbalanced masculine forces, that cause and perpetuate wars and associated horrors, that we have manifested as a representation of the level of evolution of mankind.

Moreover, as someone who used to be on the side of the oppressor, I now realise the importance of what Ali meant by "*staying on the surface*". I remember listening to the speeches of our ruling leader with my comrades... oh how much we believed that we were in the right! We had complete conviction that the oppression we were enacting was justified... I hope this can start to give one the idea of how we can go down the wrong path without questioning it all, solely because we feel that we are correct in our complex ideologies. For if there was one thing that Ali rejected, it was fanaticism and absolute conviction in any ideology. After all his mystical teachings and readings, he never even accepted the idea of an absolute God, no matter how much he admired the scholarly writings of so many religions.

Looking back now, he viewed all religion as secular metaphysics. He adopted this defensive outlook as his way of minimising the chances that: what is built from ideals, in terms of goals or dreams for the future, does not turn into a monstrosity due to blind faith. After all, humans have been known to ruin even the most sacred of things, take this planet for example. He made it clear to me that he wasn't against religion at all, and I'm confident that he wouldn't mind me becoming a devout Muslim, for example, but I think that he thought it useful to play the role of some indifferent theorist so as to spark some moral introspection within me.

Ali thought that a simple belief in the "highest good" served as an antidote potent enough to quell the evil forces that ruled the earth, and to anesthetise ideologies that attempt to outrank common sense, and love. This was the context that he believed was missing from the world.

His way of describing this was to remain mindful of something that you love - certainly - with all of your heart, be it your own family, a work of art, or a good friend. He taught me to turn this certainty toward the simple fact that: the source of our love is who we are at our essence, and this source is underneath our thoughts, psychological identities i.e. it *is* our very awareness of being. Ali is simply saying to value (or love) that which generates value (or love) and, as this has been our saving grace in even the harshest of times, we are obliged to pay respects to it, the same we do to a loyal friend.

The friend in this case, or the highest good, is that miraculous source that animates the human being; the source that allows love to exist. This was Ali's idea of truth, and it is a truth that does not require any doctrine, has no taboo and does not see anyone as higher or lower, but is a truth that exists equally within each of us, one that is up to us as individuals to find for ourselves. Ali never suggested that one throw away their faith or religion, but instead to admire the beauty of the texts and teachings of their neighbours as well as their own.

Now, I realise that this was Ali's response to a world that led us to self-deceit, a world that responds naively to tyrannical leaders and cunning mass media. A world that divides and conquers through distorting and reframing truths to justify dogmatic beliefs, attempting to make us judge our cross-continental acquaintances.

Really, I think that people, or civilians, of all countries are good people, no matter what political figureheads may have us believe. Most people have no aggressions against each other, and they like each other, often holidaying in each other's countries and enjoying each other's food and music. But the problem is that many people don't know enough about the world outside their own countries. The majority have no concern and no information about other people - many could not even find each other on a map. I think Western people are also good, but I think that many of their countries will be taken over and destroyed from the inside by various fanatical lobbies. The people do not see this as they are too busied with the responsibilities and pressures of their modern lives, but the political fanatics and tyrants will use this to gradually grab more and more power and destroy them.

What I was once a part of, but have since escaped, was a certain political fanaticism strong enough to justify the displacement of innocents in places they lived peacefully for many years. You can compare this to a time during the Second World War for example, where International Communism became strong enough to balance Christendom, which would then be restrained and held in check until the time when it would be needed for the final social cataclysm. Do we not see so many unintended consequences today, perpetrated by armies that claim to be so benevolent? How many times has the developed world hurt the very people and causes they were trying to "help" by doing something that they claimed was good, but actually caused more harm to them in the long term?

Hindsight is 20/20, but my vision for the next World War is that it would be conducted in such a way that religious republics and political fanaticism mutually destroy each other. This would unleash the nihilists and the atheists and shall provoke a great social cataclysm, which in all its horror will show clearly to all nations the effect of absolute atheism; the origins of savagery and of most bloody turmoil. Inevitably, people everywhere will be forced to defend themselves against the multitudes disillusioned with religion, whose spirits will be without direction and leadership. Humanity will be anxious for an ideal, but without knowledge of where to send its adoration. Society will receive a false light shone by tyrants through the universal manifestation of the pure doctrine of evil brought finally out into public view.

This manifestation will likely result from a general reactionary movement following the destruction of both religious ideals and atheism, both conquered and exterminated at the same time. I know this because I was inside of it, oiling the gears of this great, yet seductively subtle war machine. Now, I am obliged to share a suggestion of individual sovereignty, to a world revolving once again in the direction of tyrants and groupthink:

Almost everybody you know has a good will/intention in this life, but so did many dictators and tyrants - so we say that *"the road to hell is often paved with good intentions"*. Good intentions are therefore not enough. We must take responsibility for our own creation, as we explicitly create reality that mirrors our internal setup. Our dreams hint at this. For example, if we are not willing to accept the dark sides of ourselves, we create the picture of these dark sides as a hidden reality; a reality that shoves many unspoken horrors under the carpet: inequality, homelessness, human trafficking, environmental destruction... We must regain sovereignty of our creational powers.

Similarly, when we start to work on ourselves, our traumas, and wake up to the full scale of being a human, we unveil many dramas we never saw before; hidden pains behind good intention. We must confront our own demons in us, hence the symbolic teaching:

"Why do dragons hoard gold? Because the things you most need are always to be found where you least want to look."
– Jordan Peterson

If we judge our perpetrator as "bad" and "evil", and we see ourselves as good, poor helpless victims in this hierarchical system, all we are doing is expressing energetic disgust, which again reinforces our ego. Similarly, if we bring out our guns and revolt, all we do is reproduce bloodshed, becoming perpetrators ourselves. Alternatively, if we try to heal the poorest victims of the perpetrators, again we identify with their victimhood to be able to feel something ourselves, essentially doubling the suffering. This is primarily because our desire to heal others comes from a place of guilt, which, as Ali learnt, is the secret sibling of pride, or ego. If you choose to help others with physical charity, at least recognise the reciprocal healing benefit you will receive in return.

To me, the most effective solution to reduce the unpleasantness in this world is to focus on finding personal solutions to dissolve the negative aspects within ourselves. For example, if you judge bad behaviour in someone else, your judgement may be a reflection of your own limited perception, an aspect not in free interaction with your highest self. If you witness a questionable act, or even find yourself judging another as we all do, ask yourself: *"Where am I being caught in my own cognitive prison?*" Find and dissolve that psycho-structure as quickly as possible, in your lifetime.

In your ability to heal yourself, you are confronted with the capacity to raise children that are born free of debt, children that are wise enough to know when to listen to you, and when to listen to themselves. Children who grow to follow their heart rather than fear; their own reasoning rather than indoctrination. For this reason, I do believe that helping yourself to be at your best for others is the lightning path to creating a better world. It has always been true for this world and always will be, and if there are other worlds, it would be true for those as well. So, we heed the words of the ancient Egyptian metaphysician, and someone a little more recent:

"As above so below" - *Hermes Trismegistus, 2300BC*

"Peace at home, peace in the Universes" - *Mustafa Kemal Atatürk*

Taking responsibility for our own illumination defeats another kind of intellectual evil in this world, which I call "truth by consensus". This kind of evil is committed by people who feel inferior in their intellectual capacity, are close-minded & myopic. These are the people who operate on this doctrine of "truth by consensus", or sometimes called "peer review", which is not always the most appropriate truth-seeking tool. This is because peer review is often a tool used by academicians to gratify the opinions of those above them, in order to be accepted by the academic community and certain fiscal interests. This phenomenon can leave only agreement with the past, without any space for new, free or radical altruism in the age-old debate for truth. Truth on the most important metaphysical topics such as the nature of reality, spiritual health, consciousness, the true history and the purpose of mankind.

Now, I realise that I am beginning to sound like those fanatical utopianists that I'm warning you about, but this is just my way of composing with words. Really just like you, I am trying to figure everything out. I am trying, trying and trying, to make sense of this world and how we can make it more beautiful. And for me, the ultimate beauty is that which successfully scrapes some element of truth and meaning from a world ingrained with pain; a truth that doesn't pretend the world is anything other than what it is.

It is that beautiful, surface-level commonality in religious books that never changes. It is the unchanging proof that all revelatory inspiration was revealed from the same channel, from the same source. It is a truth that creates a world where two men do not need to agree on everything to have peace, because they agree on the most important thing.

It is that golden line of truth that thrives through each era, only becoming more polished as it is tested. I believe that the role of art is to pull down this curtain of truth, with silver linings so resplendent that the audience may see themselves in its reflection, recognising their own awe. Recognising that within themselves is a power greater than anything they have ever known, a power that heals, a power that distinguishes truth from lie. A power that contracts a universal agreement among Buddhists, Hindus, Christians, Mystics, Jews, Globalists, Muslims, Egyptians - you name it; Alchemists, Atheists, Taoists and so on... a power that is so obvious yet is so easy to miss, a power that reveals itself in the strangest moments.

You have felt it before, I know you have... for example, was there ever a time in your life where you were "in the moment" and subsequently acted with perfection and grace? Was there ever a time that, for some fluke of a reason, your self-doubt shut off for a little while and you acted with bravery and triumph? Do you remember doing or saying something so smooth and sexy without even thinking, wondering for days afterwards where that came from, or how you could "*get there*" again? If not, then I suggest you think harder and give yourself more credit.

Either way, it seems that there is some higher potential in us that reveals itself in momentous occasions. I think that this is what Ali was referring to as the "sleeping giant" that awakens when you take no thought.

Why no thought? You may ask... what's so good about not thinking? And what does this have to do with overthrowing an evil government? Have I really been spiritually radicalised by a rogue writer? And am I trying to tell the whole world how to live? To that I'd say, honestly, I think yes – I may be telling you a little how to live your life, and *yes* I may have implied that you could be contributing to the evil in this world... but rest assured this is only representative of my inability to write more elegantly. This is my first book, after all, and my wife's advice to *"write how you speak"* to help me overcome my challenges of articulation, is questionable advice, at best. Nonetheless, you have read this far – so why stop now? Let's finish this journey together. Besides, I didn't tell you about the last hoard of writing that I found in Ali's cell.

I must confess, I'm not very good at processing death and I apologize for my shortcomings. I get quite awkward when I talk about it, but I'll try my best. When I visited Ali's cell the following morning, I found him sitting in a cross-legged posture, eyes closed, just like a monk. He held his palms open, they were cold and eerily limp, and resting in them were several bunches of papers, some older than others, folded neatly together. Notably by his side were older pieces of paper, all torn up and discarded. I say again - I'm not very good with death, but I knew he was not simply asleep. Without thinking, I took the papers out of his hands and put them into my bag. I then turned around and marched, single-mindedly, out of the prison compound and never looked back.

I would like to think that Ali intended for me to find those papers and retrieve them. In retrospect, I'm sure they were carefully selected. Why else would he tear up all the other papers in the cell? What was *so* special about the particular selection stacked neatly in his hands?

Moreover, I think he had understood the real reason why his life was spared; why he was chosen to be the translator for these seemingly mystical texts. My superiors were interested in knowledge of the soul - and if we are to call it the soul, they sought to understand its constitution. They wanted to gather intelligence on the soul in the same way they would spy on a small group of revolutionaries or monitor suspicious phone call activity. They conducted such ploys in the name of "national security", leaving no stone unturned in either the physical or spiritual realm. Specifically, they wanted to learn the strengths and weaknesses of this spiritual truth and, above all, prohibit this truth from reaching the hearts of men all over the world.

They considered the soul an existential threat to their tyrannical, often psychological, operations. After all, an awakened man is much more difficult to rule over; he remains uninfluenced by promises of vanity, empty words, and false idols. No longer does he fall for the challenging delusions presented by his own mind, no more is he easily swayed by fear or pressured by outside forces. Why? Because he has found a firm footing in his own integrity, led by a successful revolt of the tyrant within himself.

Nevertheless, I doubt that Ali would spend even his most solitary days thinking about such conspiracies. Instead, I'm certain he was more concerned with helping me find the answers that I sought. I wanted to know the meaning of life and the most enlightened truths a man should know. And in the end, I feel satisfied that I achieved this.

The *first* of two topics he left for me was a translation of a lesser-known story of Adam and Eve, one that I put to the top of the pile for him to translate first. The story in his hands that he translated was fragmented and missing in pieces, but documents Adam's experiences as an archetypal journey of purpose that every man is to go through. I have done what I could to fill in the gaps and complete this story, in Ali's memory, in a latter chapter of this book.

The *second* topic is what we will cover in the next chapter, which seemed to be written by Ali on fresh paper, with the quality of his handwriting dwindling as the pages progressed. I assume that he wrote this on his final night. He articulated a succinct analysis of the mysterious consciousness power that lays dormant beneath our mind, going on to describe what happens to a man when he accesses this power.

Ali's transcripts reveal a synthesis of wisdom that I find in no other writing, either contemporary or later. They hint at the penultimate purpose of his writing career, alluding to an executive summary of the wisdom of the ages, namely, pinpointing that golden line where the creator meets the creation.

What the next chapter speaks of is specifically this wisdom of the ages; that when you strip away all of the layers of ego, social conditioning and other psychological baggage, you will find a sense of the seed of the creator; a semblance of divine energy within you. Through letting go and cutting the cords of your physical surroundings and conditioning, you get in touch with the "source", i.e. your "true self". This is said to lead to a feeling of fulfilment and trust, enabling one to view life from a place of abundance. I believe that this is the phenomenon of love-based self-sovereignty; a feeling of certainty that Ali was trying to teach me about. The feeling of recognising one's nobler qualities that seem to emerge naturally when connected with one's inner light.

I thoroughly hope that you enjoy Ali's unapologetically condensed description in the next chapter, and I hope that it helps you to look within yourself with more clarity. I added some quotes myself and filled in historical details to make the text more lucid. I believe the knowledge serves as a gentle reminder for you to take a moment to appreciate the magic of the world of life inside your core, to reconnect with yourself and allow this magical, spiritual, energy of yours to blossom. Most of all, I assume that Ali thought that the following topics best served as a framework that allow for a deeper understanding of all mystic teaching. In doing so, I believe that every person has a world of possibilities to look forward to, if only they would look within.

So for a short while, could you consider that it is possible that you can perceive something "higher" than this? We are inclined to believe that the truth of our existence is just that; we are some evolved bacteria living on a small watery rock, and that life is all just one big, scientific, coincidence. However, ancient (e.g. Vedic) texts remind us that at one point in our past we were much more evolved in our nature, sciences, architecture and philosophy. They describe that, in comparison, humanity declined, and we became more disconnected with our truth and our potential than ever before. Could this be true, or is this just another delusion to give us hope? Can we ever experience real, divine, and inspirational magic in our lifetimes? Or is this just against common sense?

It is very common for us to reject information at first glance, only to realise that it was true when it was given more time and consideration. For example, at different vantage points in our life, we have changing perceptions towards things. You may come back to this book a month later and have a completely different perception of it - I'd ask you to try it. Sometimes when you experience leaps of faith, perhaps during meditation or trying new habits, it is only afterwards that you realise they actually worked. It's a similar phenomenon of not knowing how a clock works, but still trusting it to keep the time. Likewise, we could try to trust a new and mysterious, bio-mechanical practice to bring forth fresh and useful insights to our lives.

Likewise, you may trust the way some people live, how they walked their path and, based on their results, try out what they practice - until you notice your own results. You can give yourself the luxury of a reasonable amount of educated faith, just enough to take you to the next step of your development. Your faith can increase with small degrees of outcomes that will work for you over time. Besides, we don't always have to use analytical science to apply new principles to our lives. Some of the most motivated, successful people are themselves a little bit deluded. This is an art in itself. Moreover, life is a massive mystery - and at the end of the day, what the hell do we know?

Our real transformation occurs when we take the time to self-inspect, as we become empowered to make our own more purposeful meanings, and create a new world. When you reflect on the thoughts from the most evolved minds and inspirational people, you can still decide for yourself whether the words ring true to you. In this way, you carve out the advancement of your own thoughts, making your mind an even more beautiful place to be. Only you can give this gift to yourself; the prize of discovering what you are really made of.

Isaac Newton believed that the cosmos had deep encoded messages within it about our, and its, origins. He believed that this knowledge had been placed there, so that we would be able to decode them once we had evolved sufficient intelligence. Newton was the first to translate into Latin the work of the legendary Hellenistic figure, Hermes

Trismegistus (who originated as a syncretic combination of the Greek God Hermes and the Egyptian God Thoth). Nevertheless, that which is soundless within us remains a mystery, and perhaps we should not expect otherwise. Science is about observation over time, something that can be proven. Science explains material matter, what has been made which we are able to recognise and observe. But it is away from this recognition that miracles begin. If only created material matter exists, neither poetry nor philosophy nor Beethoven's music would exist – nor you or I. And even if all scientific puzzles were solved, the spiritual mystery of existence itself would still remain.

In any case, have you ever felt that there is more to you than meets the eye? Have you a deep yearning for evolving your perception? What if you have more than what it takes to create a better world? Do you want to get closer to *your* essence, whose power heals the closer you get to it?

Out of all-inclusive, unconditional compassion comes the healing of not only yourself but of all mankind. Therefore, everything you see happening is the consequence of that which you are, thus the responsibility sets on you.

You have the power to create a new world, a noble story yet to be told.

CHAPTER

10

So, let's take a look at these mysterious pages I found in Ali's hands...

How do you search for a needle in a haystack? Burn the haystack down and you find the needle easily.

So Rumi once said: "Past and future veil God from our sight; Burn up both of them with fire"

Why the incendiary words from an arsonist man? What are we to destroy so peacefully?

And what of the Greek fire of the Byzantine? How they heavily guarded their chemical formula, a mystical flame remaining alight on the surface of rivers, dazzling their foes with fear.

Knowledge of the extraordinary fire is the eternal conquest of man, who destroys and conquers wherever he may go.

And what of the fire within himself?

Faith befriends the man who seeks endlessly, forever inwards may he steer.

May he find the source of his flame, a solitary kingdom, through silence he may hear.

The ancient Greek wordsmiths named "via negativa" as their grammatical chisel, who chipped away at falsehood with the sharp edges of their intellect, revealing an indescribable truth that concealed inside. "Anatta" or "non-self" as the Buddhi's would call it, the unending and permanent aspect of reality. The "signal" in the radio body, the charioteer of the chariot body, the Son of the Sun shining over the knowledge tree.

How many saints of the ages have spoken of the source that is within thee? Do you sense what power you possess? If I could show you truly, I would raise a mirror to your face, but it would leave you blind. Alas, here we are reduced to words, bound by time and distance, still I shall describe for you the sacred integrity of your own mind.

But what is the mind? A collection of thoughts, calculations, and memories? In the yogic understanding, there are sixteen different words to describe the human mind at great distance. Sixteen! O' how we have simplified our definition of the most important creation in existence. So often do we turn to our ancestors for the instruction manual to our conscious machine. These sixteen words, or dimensions, fall into four classes.

In order of the surface to the deepest layers of mind, the names of these categories are: Buddhi (logic or intellect), Manas (bank of memory), Ahankara (sense of identity/ego), and Chitta (cosmic consciousness).

Understanding the deepest layers of your mind leads to the purification of false belief systems that underlie the karmic repetitions and patterns of self-defeat. It is the sadomasochistic engagement with the illusory self that produces evermore uncertainty, guilt and shame; the weight of sin and failure and defeat, and all melodramatic elements that the ego loves to have to deal with. For the ego wants to prove that it can eventually do the impossible by overcoming these tremendous obstacles and finally, like the story of Sisyphus, get that stone up the hill and keep it there. But no, it will always roll back down once again. It is this game that the ego likes to play that prolongs its delusional lifespan.

But a point comes when the game loses its taste, and the taste of purification becomes a far more interesting diet. And it's when the dispassion for the dream, and the passion for the awakening from the dream, have reached a tipping point that the awakening is unstoppable. Soon, the dream itself morphs from a nightmare and emerges into the beauty and goodness of creation itself. A beauty that is inherent in our hearts, waiting to blossom once again. In that blossoming, the egoic emptiness can finally be filled with the blissful intelligence of that cosmic consciousness, revealing a purposeful intelligence that was always who you really are.

Thus, life is a process of experiencing the horror of forgetting who and what you are, as well as the pleasure of remembering, so that you may never forget again. Each man is destined to this process of unlearning and learning, of knowing thyself so that one can become thyself.

Meditation's purpose is to enable you to penetrate the false self to find the source of who you are. It is only through silence, wakeful devoted silence, silence surrendered to ultimate reality that enables the accumulation of spiritual energy that dissolves the falsehoods of the mind. The goal of meditation is not to leave the world behind but to come into the real, and then to return to the unreal world and bring the real into it.

Our true empowerment comes from liberation from all identity structures, and the refusal to interrupt the connection with the flow of cosmic consciousness that emerges through silence. To demystify such a claim, we must understand the anatomy of the mind, layer by layer:

BUDDHI - THE INTELLECT [LOGIC]

Buddhi is the logical dimension of thought, and what modern education systems and modern sciences have largely limited themselves to. That is a buddhu (foolish) way of existence.

The intellect is designed to reason on top of the data gathered from experience. Thus, it will not take you beyond anything further than your own current dimension. You must look deeper.

"The intellect has little to do on the road to discovery. There comes a leap in consciousness, call it intuition or what you will, the solution comes to you, but you do not know how, or why" – Einstein.

MANAS — MEMORY RESERVE [YOUR KARMA]

Your mind and body hold memory stored DNA from your oldest ancestors, hence your appearance and your generational traumas. This is also referred to as your karma, as karma is interchangeably used to refer to memory; your past, or destiny due to cause/effect.

Manas is also held in the brain, to store memories that you may draw from to solve intellectual problems and gain a narrative for your decision making and sense of self.

AHANKARA — SENSE OF IDENTITY [EGO]

Going even deeper, Ahankara can also be understood as the identity, or ego, which provides the context for your intellect to function, and for your memory to associate itself with. Your intellect is as enslaved to your identity as it is to your memories. But you are much more than this; more than your name, nation, your beliefs or your community.

There is a power that runs below all of this, and that runs all of this. Transcending your sense of identity is the final step toward your evolution.

CHITTA — COSMIC CONSCIOUSNESS [THE SACRED FIRE]

The purest, most base layer of the mind is called Chitta, also known as "chitagni" (meaning inner fire). Chitta is the fire that powers the furnace of your mind. The source of this fire is that undiscoverable spiritual element of the cosmos.

Chitta is always on, whether one is awake or asleep, it goes on conducting your breath, powering the intelligence behind the cells that perform a billion calculations a minute. Chitta is the undeniable non-being essentiality that allows existence to be validated by your subjective conscious experience. If one touches this dimension of mind, then the spirit, or as yogis say: Shiva, becomes your servant.

"The Spirit helps with everything, like a young man trying to support a family. We, like the young man's wife, stay home, taking care of the house, nursing the children. Spirit and matter work together like this, in a division of labour" - Rumi

One is rewarded with an unshakeable presence when they have learnt to consciously access their Chitta. These people wear a mesmerising glow in their eyes, they leak a constant fountain of cosmic energy, of intelligence, of inspiration. The Chitta is the core of "mind/spirit" that is the closest to the almighty, absolute consciousness of the creator. Also called "nous" in Greek, or "anim" in Latin (to be "animated"), referred to as "the friend" by Sufis and the "only begotten son" by gnostic Christians. Many traditions throughout time have named this life-giving force appearing in all dimensions of the body-mind:

LIGHT | SPIRIT | SOUL | KUNDALINI SHAKTI | THUMOS | CHI | PRANA | VRILL | JOON

It is the universal consciousness, oneness with God, manifested by Jesus, Krishna, and other avatars. Great saints and yogis know it as the state of samadhi meditation, wherein their consciousness has become identified with the divine intelligence in every particle of creation; they feel the entire Universe as their own body. Chitta is the Alpha & Omega, the crux of Wisdom and Samadhi (meditation/absorption/Jnana) in Buddhism. Samadhi is the meditative activity that is the culmination of the noble Eight-fold path of enlightenment, of transcending physical existence. It is for making the Chitta sovereign and resolving ignorance into wisdom, i.e. the full and complete synthesis of the Chitta unto itself. Gnosis (deep knowledge of spirituality) and purified Chitta (Chitta Vishudhya) is how one is called a Buddha, an enlightened one, a Sun God etc. The purification of Chitta is equal to "Buddhahood"; your true nature revealing itself through all derivatives of this North Star.

No other noun is given as much importance as Chitta, which is given 17 different designations in Buddhist scripture, as follows:

- The purification of one's own Chitta is among the most important aspects of Buddhism (mentioned in Buddhasasana - the Doctrine of the Buddha).

- The Chitta is the only noun in scripture which is said to obtain a state of being "taintless/unpolluted" (Anasava).

- Chitta is the only thing which is said to be obtained or gathered within the realm of immortality.

- The Chitta is said to be the basis (armana) for Parinirvana (Nirvana after death) in the Pali manuscripts. With an enlightened Chitta, Gautama Buddha was able to see the limitlessness of the Chitta after he left the mortal realm (death). This enlightened state led to his Chitta being liberated (Ahu). An unshakeable, liberated Chitta does not cling to physical concerns and reaches Parinirvana.

- Chitta is the only thing which is differentiated from the five skandhas (aggregates) (rupa/vedana/samjna/ samskara/vijnana); i.e., "*Whatever form, feelings, perceptions, experiences, or consciousness there is (the 5 skandhas), these he sees to be without permanence, as suffering, as ill, as a plague, a boil, a sting, a pain (dukha) pain, an affliction, as foreign, as otherness, as empty (suññata), as Selfless (anattata).*

So he turns his consciousness (Chitta) away from these; therein he gathers his consciousness within the realm of Immortality (amataya dhatuya). This is tranquility; this is that which is most excellent!"

- Chitta is the only thing said to be perfected by samadhi (meditative state) and panna (wisdom). The purification of the light (jyoti) within one's own Chitta, is the very soul/truth (atman).

- With a steadfast and supremely fixed Chitta, and a Chitta emancipated from ignorance (avidya), the soul becomes Brahma - one with the Universe. The collected and quelled Chitta is the Supreme Soul (mahatma). Chitta is said to be the basis/medium for the recollection (smruti) of past lives.

- Chitta is said to be its own foundation (anirmana - without any other foundation except itself), hence making the Chitta the "absolute". The sovereign mind (Chitta) which is its own support (anirmana) is the foundation, making it equal to the soul (atman).

- Chitta is the only thing comparable to an indestructible diamond. One who has destroyed a tainted Chitta has liberated the wisdom trapped in the polluted Chitta (Chitta vimutta and panna vimutta - the two types of liberation also spoken of in Advaita Vedanta and the Upanishads). The diamond-like Chitta is made perfect by wisdom and samadhi.

- The entire Aryan Eight-fold path (ariya atthangika magga) is itself said to be both *"being"* and *"ending with"* Chitta as its basis. The path of Brahmacarya (monastic life) is not lived for the sake of gains, honours or acclaim, nor for virtue's sake. This monastic life is lived for the sole purpose of the emancipation of the Chitta alone, which is the quintessential final core.

- The Chitta is what is said to *"go towards the light"* i.e. the heaven realm in Buddhism, of obtaining the absolute (not like Judeo-Christian interpretations of Heaven, but of the gnostic *"seek ye first the kingdom of heaven [within you] and all things shall be added unto you"*).

- Chitta is the only thing that is said to achieve freedom from ignorance and agnosis. A steadfast Chitta is emancipated from sensual desires and avidya (ignorance).

- Chitta is the only noun that achieves complete liberation and emancipation. The Chitta (mind) and the spirit/self are not differentiated, thus, a liberated Chitta means a liberated spirit/self. The Chitta is the sole basis of the Superior Path.

- The Aryan path is endowed with the taintless Chitta.

- (Emancipation of) Chitta is deemed to be the "*highest absolute*". Of all types of unmanifested emancipations of the Chitta, the fixed and unshakeable emancipation of the Chitta is the Highest Supernal.

- The entire basis of Buddhism is said to be for, and in regards to, the Chitta. The purification of one's own Chitta is the doctrine of the Buddha. Vimutta Chitta (emancipated/liberated mind) equals "Buddhahood".

- The Chitta is deemed to achieve freedom from becoming (bhava). The Chitta can transcend causation and cannot be denied.

"*My Chitta, emancipated from sorrows, from becoming (bhava), from nescience/ignorance/agnosis (avidya). There exists no fruit more exquisite than this (emancipation of the mind).*"

"*For a long time I have been cheated, tricked and hoodwinked by my Chitta. For when grasping, I have been grasping onto form, for when grasping, I have been grasping onto feelings, for when grasping, I have been grasping onto perceptions, for when grasping, I have been grasping onto experiences, for when grasping, I have been grasping onto consciousness.*"

The Chitta is a cosmic energy that, when made to expand, brings great joy and bliss. It leads to the epistrophe (Greek term for "return"); negation of the culmination of via negativa, spiritual apophysis (Greek term for understanding the Divine will) - all that which you are *not*. This is the final fruition of human spiritual development.

The awakening of this cosmic energy has often been symbolised as the rising of a serpent, which is referred to as "kundalini shakti". Kundalini (chitti) being pure creative force and "shakti" made up of ananda (bliss), chit (pure awareness), and prema (love). It is said that after the Universe was created, there was excess electromagnetic energy left over. Ultimately, this excess energy was bundled up and placed at the base of every human being's spine as kundalini. This is our psycho-social heritage; a dynamic energy which takes the human being to the divine consciousness. The spiritual purpose of the human is to awaken their kundalini through certain yogic/meditative exercises.

Through kundalini kriya yoga, the kundalini "fire" at the base of the spine is gradually released, taking the trapped soul (atman) step by step, chakra by chakra, to Sahasrara (the corona/crown chakra of the skull). This fire burns the karma surrounding our polluted soul (the illusory layers of intellect, memory and ego). Our corona chakra is finally "activated" to that which is higher, drawing in revelatory insight. Dissolving the illusory dream that our soul is trapped in unveils our highest potential of being.

- Kundalini (chitti) is the mother

- Chitta is the father consciousness

- The soul (chaitanya or atman), entrapped in the senses and layers of the mind, is the son (which needs to be rescued)

- The final goal is to raise the troubled son/soul up to meet the father/supreme/divine consciousness (Chitta, or sometimes symbolically referred to as Shiva), which the soul must be fused in

Kundalini energy is a "mother" energy; the cosmic energy we are born from, often also symbolised in religious texts as the "divine mother". In other words, the kundalini (chitti) mother rushes up the chimney of the spine, with her son (chaitanya or atman), to meet her Lord (Chitta) at the crown of the skull (Sahasrara, also called the Thousand Petaled Lotus).

Note the subtly overlapping translations and elements. Such is the state of affairs of our core spiritual truth. Such is the attempt to encapsulate the subtlest vibrations of the Universe into words. I want you to see where the knowledge transfer blurs the essence of truth throughout the ages. All you must know is: there exists a lightning path available for you to reach the divine consciousness, through the practice of kundalini kriya yoga. This is the great cosmic secret; the crown jewel of the ages. The ultimate truth is through experience. You must become God to understand God, to truly have proof of God; not to hear about him, study him, to read accounts of him or to have faith. Throw your faith out of the window and experience the truth for yourself. God has placed himself inside you, it is up to you to search intelligently within.

Think, think, think and use the magnificent brain you have been gifted. Throw away all taboo and *experience* the *knowing*, become the ultimate being. Read, read, read widely, search indiscriminately for the truth of yourself.

To reiterate and delve deeper, our bodies contain a plethora of nerve centres containing varying forms of memory, intelligence and energy. The most powerful symbolic interpretation takes the form of a coiled serpent-like energy lying mostly dormant at the base of our spines containing "chit kundalini" which, through yogic practices, can be channelled up our spine all the way to meet our brain matter. The symbol of the snake is one that has been known since the beginning of time, including in the story of Adam and Eve as the bringer of knowledge -

perhaps by coincidence. The snake, in kundalini symbolism, is expressed as raising up the spine in a double-helix fashion, reminiscent of a DNA spiral, and/or as we now understand, a polarising electromagnetic energy (with a positive node at the brain and a negative node at the base of our spine). The transfer of this energy has recently been captured on advanced medical imaging devices. Now, in modern times, the image of a snake entwined in a downward-spiral shape around a rod symbolizes medicine and health care services. The Greeks regarded snakes as sacred, using them in healing rituals to honour Asclepius, the Greco-Roman God of medicine, as snake's skin-shedding was viewed as a symbol of rebirth and renewal.

This renewal has been symbolised by yogic cultures as "burning" one's karma - karma meaning memory. This memory is stored in various centres (or chakras) in our body e.g. our brain, heart and gut - which we now know are all organs that contain neurons. We also now know that "trauma" is stored in the body as varying forms of memory - something the yogis knew quite some time ago. This trauma memory is both conscious and subconscious. Our memories are the cause of our emotions, which largely dictate our fate. So, in a way, we can view the kundalini fire as burning/dissolving the emotional residue of our past. The memories are still there, but we are not attached to them.

What would this mean? It would mean that you are no longer defined by your past. It would mean that you have transcended the prison of cause and effect, instead, *being* at the cause yourself. This is a significant milestone in the spiritual evolution of man. Imagine a computer writing its own code, instead of being a slave of its pre-written code. For a computer, singularity is achieved through a gradual increase in processing capacity. For a human, liberation is achieved through a gradual increase in focus on their inner fire; Chitta.

Chitta is the direction one leans towards when one gives the command to the mind to be silent, to be in stillness; not producing thoughts or images or emotions but allowing oneself to enjoy the quietude of presence that is free of thoughts. One must let the mind stop any galloping and enter into the mental oblivion; the nothingness, the emptiness of the thought-free consciousness. This is through bringing your attention deep into your wisdom body. Here, there is an instinctive understanding of the presence of God, within an understanding of the archetypal nature of consciousness that draws its energy from the source of *being*.

This is Chitta; the ultimate destination with no location, no time or space. This is where one begins to feel the shift from individual consciousness into "God's" consciousness. One's attention soon attunes itself to the presence of *something higher*, within the presence of the source of awareness; of cosmic intelligence.

Chitta is *that* power from *that* source, gained by drawing one's attention into the bliss body, into the inner light, into the space of pure spirit; of Brahman. Chitta is the great mystery of the cosmos that cannot be reached by thought, but is the purest essence of "*I am-ness*", existing in the luminous space of the absolute self.

The noise, the exterior, the traumas and obsessions burn away, dissolving in the all-seeing eye of the Chitta. The charge of the past fades into extinction, as one shines their own light of liberation onto their demons and fears, revealing their counterfeit weight of importance. This is the reward of utmost devotion to the integrity of one's own inner light. It is the source code of all archetypal parables, symbols, stories and convictions. It is Abraham sacrificing his Son (his symbolic self/troubled soul) to the Lord, it is the symbolic dance of Shiva, burning karma through the eternal cycle of birth and death. It is the flame of the whirling Sufi and the almighty Lord that rests *nearer* than your jugular vein; nearer than your physical body.

Gained through total surrender to the source of your *being-ness*, and surrender to the will, the power and the love of that presence. Until, your heart and God's presence; the purity of love and light, become one. This is embodied cleanliness, for all that remains is *that* cosmic consciousness, the self-aware miracle, the Universe itself; *you*, the egoless genius. The *clear* version of *you* that accesses the blissful intelligence of your cosmic consciousness through a strengthening of your inner light. The light that reveals your true self, your highest nature, your purest intention, your most genuine path; your life's purpose.

But enough of this spiritual speak, this kind of talk can prove to be more frustrating than useful. I will now describe the archetypal ideal man; the divine character that reveals itself when one's ego successfully morphs into the vessel of this higher intelligence. By reading and making note of these character traits, you can attain the end-result of spiritual development, providing an example for others to do the same.

This is what truth looks and feels like:

I. SELF-WORTH

With the weight of the ego lifted, the awakened man is aware of the divine, simple, consciousness-based nature of his being. For this reason, he knows that comparison is an illusion, so he chooses collaboration over competition. He begins to feel a healthy entitlement to positive experiences, and is not afraid to take up the time from someone he finds compelling. In doing so, he approaches people from a place of joy, sharing a grounded energy of love that leaks out from the centre of his being.

2. SELF-AMUSEMENT

He is at the cause and not the effect of his emotions. He is able to have fun without needing anything from anyone or the outside world. He has regained a personal power that is often lost in attachment to other people's behaviour. He is the centre of energy wherever he goes.

3. FREEDOM FROM OUTCOME

With the ability to self-amuse, he is more concerned with the process rather than the fruits of his actions. This allows him to access his flow and produce his best work, as he is free from the fog of obsession and impatience that limit one's critical thinking abilities.

4. CLARITY OF INTENTION [PURPOSE]

Intention is a purpose formed by directing the mind towards an object. Clarity of intention means that he is certain of what he wants; his purpose, with minimal resistance, doubt or hesitancy in his thinking. The clearer he gets with his intent, the better his results. He does not self-sabotage or procrastinate as his intentions are not in conflict. Most importantly, he is not defined by his past, but by a vision of his future (intention enforces self-worth).

5. CONGRUENCE

As such, his thoughts, words & actions are in complete alignment. His actions flow from his being. He is comfortable being himself but he is considerate of others' needs. Thus, he has very little self-monitoring; charisma is his second nature. People gravitate towards his energy because they sense that it is genuine.

6. SELF-AWARENESS

His mind, unshackled from the weight of the past, of discomfort, has room to think clearly. His body, unsullied by old feelings of discomfort, allows him to relax into the moment. His sharpened focus enhances his ability to be aware of the needs of the person in front of him.

Finally, his humility causes him to care about them. In this way, he is the light of this world.

Above all, he learns from everyone else, but comes up with a method of thinking, communicating and being that is uniquely comfortable for him. As such, he learns from new experiences, but owns what he learns. He keeps moving forward, his heart as open as the sky. He allows his mind and heart to melt completely into the beloved. He rests in the purity of indifferent observation, to bring goodness and the power of redemption into the dream field of the world.

And what of yourself? I ask again: do you not sense what power you possess?

Feel this power of supreme presence permeating the electromagnetic nerve endings through your veins. Feel what it's like to be present again in the world, but not of it. Feel what it's like to be completely unburdened by the hooks of undesirable memories, attachment, fear or anxiety - to be liberated from the dream of the ego, until even the dream field is only the presence of that divine self. The *self* that is *pretending* to be the psycho-drama, but that is now returning to the singularity so the soul can be redeemed. Feel how it is to be bodiless while in the body, egoless and yet with the capacity for thought, silent even when the organism is making sound, or hearing sound.

Understand the sense, the nonsense and the transcendence of sins, free of belief in what appears in the mind matrix, sustained by the eternal presence of the real and the immortal, even within the mortal frame. Luminous even in the darkness of the world and real within the unreal, untouched by the dream, o' homesick you!

"And as Moses lifted up the serpent in the wilderness, even as the son of man be lifted up: That whosoever believeth in him should not perish but have eternal life" - John 3:14–15

To add more context, the ancients have named this firesome, snake-symbolised light/energy by the work of various deities, Gods, Goddesses, angels and divinities, each with a sacred story of the Universe. These stories describe the intention of the cosmos; straining to give birth to Sun Gods, referring to our own unattained, but attainable state. The Egyptian Legend of Osiris, The Babylonian Enuma Elish, the Norse's creation myth, The Korean Legend of Dan Gun, The Tibetan scriptures, the Navajo Story of Emergence, the Maya's Popol Vuh, the Emerald Tablets of Thoth and many other mythologies all underline the same symbolic creation of the awakening. It is why you see an uraeus snake so proudly gliding out of the forehead of iconic ancient Egyptian statues. This snake is seen as a symbol of sovereignty, royalty, deity and authority through divine awakening of this life-force energy.

The most prominent of these figures is the African-born prophet, Thoth, identified by the Greeks with Hermes

Trismegistus (the Thrice Great), recognised by some scriptures as the Son of the Sun God, Ra. It is said that Thoth created himself through the power of language and is the creator of magic, the inventor of writing, teacher of man, the messenger of the Gods, and the divine recordkeeper and mediator.

Described as the *"faceless prophet"* by the Islamicist Pierre Lory, it was said that scribes would pour out one drop of their ink in Thoth's (Hermes') honour before they began their daily work. Hagiographers and chroniclers of the first centuries of the Islamic Hajira identified Hermes with Idris, the Islamic prophet of Surahs 19.57 and 21.85 in the Quran. Thoth was said to be the original "Sun God", with accounts of his influence from as early as the lost civilisation of Atlantis, some calling him an Atlantean *"priest-king"*. Thoth was an initiator into the mysteries of the divine science and wisdom that animates the world; he carved the principles of this sacred science in the fabled "Emerald Tablets", translated into Ancient Greek by Alexandrian scholars around 330 B.C. After that, it was reportedly buried by Alexander the Great, somewhere on the Giza Plateau.

The Emerald Tablets are said to reveal the original wisdom for initiates to develop the power of alchemical thinking; to access that which is inherent within one, but lies dormant. One must spark the "secret fire" of consciousness to receive personal gnosis, in a way combining logic with feeling so that the fire is percolating from deep within. That is to say, by following the outlined formula, one would become themselves a Hermes Trismegistus: the perfected man.

The Emerald Tablets were said to provide the recipe for producing the philosopher's stone; the supreme object of alchemy, the highest state of consciousness. Shihaboddin Sohravardi, a leading figure of the illuminationist school of Islamic philosophy, speaks symbolically of this stone as being an emerald colour, one powerful enough to tint the celestial realm green. For the Sufi, emerald is a symbol of the cosmic soul. An emerald stone is said to have fallen from the crown of Lucifer during his battle with God, representing the fall of a sacred knowledge of mankind. Ancient Romans felt that the very soul of an individual was restored to its peak when they wore the emerald stone. This peak is also known as "Mount Qaf" in Persian symbology, it is the highest peak in the centre of man's psyche; the world one encounters in mystical experiences.

"Qaf, the Cosmic Mountain. whose summit is none other than the most elevated of man's psyche. On the summit one finds the emerald rock which tints the heavenly vault green" – Christian Rebiase

Many of the translations, commentaries, and replicas are ancient themselves, including writings from Adonis and Aristotle. The Arabic translation of the tablet, written by Jabir ibn Hayyan around 800AD was then also translated in Latin by Sir Isaac Newton. Numerous false interpretations and commentaries of Hermes's works have ensued, some claiming the Emerald Tablets to date back to 36,000BC, none of which substantiate a compelling source. Many are those who cite the text but do not understand it, and the original tablet is yet to be found. Some Jewish mystics identify the tablet's author with Seth, the second son of Adam. They say that the tablet was taken aboard the ark by Noah, and that after the flood, Noah hid the tablet in a cave near Hebron, where it was later discovered by Sarah, the wife of Abraham. Regardless, evidence to support the case for an actual artifact is based only on reports in written records and allegations. Nobody can claim if the Emerald Tablet is either a legend or if it really existed.

Oh, was I hoping to open my eyes one morning to see an emerald slate resting on the prison floor, waiting for me to run my hands across its archaic Cuneiform wisdom like a blind man scanning a braille bible. Could it be that another asset of humanity is locked away, hidden from us in the Vatican archives? Perhaps I will know in another life. And what does this mean for you, curious reader of my hopeful notes? You, who hold the secrets of your mind, the crown jewel of the buddhas, the lineage of the prophets, the cryptic Atlantean archetype... am I yet to drive you insane? Or have I already succeeded in my pursuit?

To show you where the trail of truth runs dry, where history fades into obscurity... where the muon radar of our archaeologists fires into the Great Pyramids, revealing nothing but foundations of sand below.

"The excavator digs, until he can see the end of the difference between the monstrous work and himself. His ends is to confirm that his thoughts live along the whole line of temples, and they live again to the mind, or are now" – Ralph Emerson

How we are like those children who play in the sand, building castles so ambitiously while our parents watch over us silently, waiting for us to retire from our laborious games. There may be moments where, by sheer persistence and enjoyment of toil, we dig out a softened green shard from a glass bottle or a little shell to proudly show our parents, who gladly retain such findings as sentimental mantelpieces. How we grow to see our little attainments as mere sentimental toys, as we eventually turn to our parents to seek their treasured wisdom; their silent understanding. To seek from our own initiative the source of their peace, their patience, their humble certainty. To begin to recognise our own rejected thoughts in the most sacred of texts, realising the sanctity of our own mind. As the Persian prophet once said:

"Ability in man is knowledge that emanates from a divine light" – *Zoroaster*

Alas, there are things which explanations can only explain away. For instance, what does it mean to you to *read* about the great, revered seasonal Indian mangos, if you cannot *taste* them for yourself? Likewise, what does it mean to you if the greatest saints and sages absorbed knowledge from a single source, if you do not see yourself in that source? And what does it matter to you if an Emerald Tablet were 38,000 years old? Are you not the subject and the matter of the sacred philosopher's stone? When do we climb out of the rabbit hole and view each story from the bird's eye? To view the similarity of the holes that humans have dug since the dawn of man. To see the same archetypal story, of burning the illusions of the mind with a sacred serpentine flame, recognising instead the miracle of divine consciousness that sleeps within us all. Giving attention to that which deserves attention; our own inner light. So the story goes:

Consciousness must be differentiated and distanced from the traditional understanding of the mind (ego). Understanding this distance brings wisdom and power because one is no longer directly within the gravitational field of the ego. Understanding this means that one is now being pulled by the soul toward the higher levels of consciousness. This then keeps the soul honest in the gradual trek up to Mount Qaf, to Paradiso, to the divine consciousness, the Lord, the father, Shiva or whatever socio-cultural interpretation of the divine remains. It is here that the mind, through that purgatory process, is gradually freed from all of its projections and illusions.

For the mind must become that zero-point of total openness, where multiple possibilities and conflicting ideas are able to co-exist peacefully. So we go through this journey in time, slowly or quickly, but that is only at the level of appearance, because we are always already in paradise! Our role is to remember what we have forgotten, and to gradually unveil our true, blessed, nature.

The lightning path is sitting silently, watching as the mind's projections arise, accepting that the projections will continue. But this time enjoying it, as you hold the knowledge to identify the sense of humour that the creator has put into himself, in this ridiculous scenario that you're in - that we are all in. And by beginning to laugh at it, and not taking it seriously, then you have shifted your relationship to it. This is truly staying on the surface; the middle way of engaging but not identifying, of tasting the bait without being caught in the trap. Over time, you will no longer entertain ridiculous situations because you know that you deserve better. You deserve freedom in all forms; freedom from your past, to recognise that the past has a plan for you until you let go of it.

And as long as you believe, *"oh, this is my fate"*, or *"I need to do this"*, and *"I need to have this"* - that whole tyrannical desperation of trying to *get* something that doesn't exist, will continue to function. But once you recognize those to be a delusion, and you are able to laugh at the delusion, then you will be halfway out of it. You will be walking the path of the "Sun Gods", as we say.

And when you ask *"well, who is aware of the delusion?"*, then you will find a being of truth; a being who is laughing and who is already able to extinguish the reappearance of those events. Yet it only repeats if you still have something to learn from it. Until you have fully decided to let go of holding whatever opinion or belief that has caused it to appear.

You will be the one who conquers the middle, indifferent path. You will be the one who dissolves these delusions with the fire of your awareness, showing the way for others to do the same. You may even gain a heightened focus of your own expertise that will still remain very valuable for society, but you shall enjoy it with a sense of humour. For in recognising all of these delusions, and by not buying into them but instead being able to laugh at them, the ego will gradually morph into a vessel of this higher intelligence that sees through its game.

Soon the ego that you hate, or that hates itself, will purify itself through the fiery love of the heart. So the love that heals has to come from your own heart, and it's this love that will reabsorb it back into its higher nature of the soul. But love is the medicine that you have to give to yourself, and I would administer it many times a day. Yes, many times a day, until you remember, until you remember, again, and again, and again - who you really are.

A wise man once said that silence is the language of God, all else is poor translation

_____ [Ali's writing became unintelligible after this point. *Now I shall be silent, and let the silence divide that which is true from that which lies -* is the rest of the sentence; he was quoting Rumi. I have added some notes in the rest of this chapter to add a further dimension of relatability to Ali's densely packed writing. I know I certainly needed a break to ponder on his guidance. Rest in peace, Ali. If only you were here to see what a blessing you have been to me. If only my work could one day make you so proud.]

I think that Ali was attempting to paint an undeniable picture of a dynamic, intelligent energy that runs through us all. He says that we have become disconnected from the larger source of this energy, and in doing so have felt weak, insecure and lacking in certainty. While Ali points to a plethora of sources and similarities between the wisdom of the ages, he wants us to ask, *"what is this all saying?"* – without going too deep into any single belief system. He wants us to question what we should *do* with this spiritual wisdom. And while he highlights the importance of such wisdom, he is quick to do away with its significance.

I believe that Ali wants us to read religious, and more esoteric, material as a means of building a certain level of curiosity, enough to get us to sit down with ourselves and to see what all the fuss is about.

Above all, Ali wanted each person to source their sense of certainty from a personal, inner experience that they have within themselves, rather than trust the words of famous scribes. Each person can choose to follow their own practice to find their own answers; their own peace. Every practice may require discipline and willpower, but will allow one to access the treasure of their truth; life path, or *purpose*, if you will - particularly from their own inner light, and nobody else's.

As an ongoing process, if one were to embark on this journey, indicators of progression each day would include overcoming any fear and doubt related to being oneself. Therefore, it is important for one to embrace their sensitivity as it represents wakefulness and competency. Sensitivity allows one to give their gift of love and accurately own who they are.

As a fundamental principle, to unleash this focused, warrior-like, force within, one must relax within their own self-trust. This ongoing process is a service to truth, and a dedication to one's fullest potential. Mistakes will still be made on this path, however, they will be easier to forgive.

Why? Because mistakes we make in our pursuit of truth serve as lessons, relevant to a journey that we wholeheartedly feel is our purpose to embark on.

SIGNS OF PROGRESS

- Higher energy and enthusiasm
- Calm and enthusiastic under stress
- Think clearly and effectively
- Great confidence and compassion
- Feel joy from smaller things
- Physical and psychic abilities efficient
- Strength of manifestation
- Ability to express your true self

LACK OF PROGRESS

- Poor health
- Weak and tired
- Irritable and anxious under stress
- Thinking muddled
- Lack of confidence
- Little empathy
- Generally unhappy
- True self is hard to express

I would refer to Ali's description of accessing one's light/Chitta/spirit and to understand the nuances of navigating thought forms whilst sitting in a meditative state. Unfortunately, I cannot recommend you undertake a practice of kundalini kriya yoga as my own research has shown it to be quite dangerous if not supervised by the right practitioner. Many have lost themselves in the process, and found it immensely difficult to integrate their experience of sudden enlightenment into their daily, modern lives.

Practically, what I would recommend is the simple act of starting your day with a silent meditation. The kind of meditation that helps you to gradually realise you are not those thoughts; that inner narrative that goes ticking away 24/7. At the core of your being, at your true state, you are more than that. You are pure awareness – with a role to play in this life. Here is a good start: *author.vision/meditation*

Soon, you will find yourself simplifying your life, where you only have to be at one place at a time, while you become more able to set time aside to be still and silent. The true goal is in discovering and working towards what you believe in, often in conflict with what the noise of the outside world has in store for you. From that place of silent clarity, you have enough focus to make informed, noble, un-traumatised decisions that best serve you and the world. This is also described as acting from your "higher self".

Practice being mindful so that you are witnessing the ego going through its roleplay, but that you are not "it". Take seriously your silent presence, the awareness behind your thoughts. You, the Spirit; the Soul, are the observer, not the thoughts themselves. The more and more you take Spirit as yourself, the more power you will have to change your role in life to one that serves your goal of self-realisation. You will access more energy to work towards your outer purpose, whilst mastering your cosmic inner purpose which is the realisation of who you really are.

And when it happens, be it with love, friendship or a career or any path you're taking - you will *just know*. There will be a smile, an inner smile, that says, *"Yes, this is it"*, or *"I found it"*, or *"I'm supposed to be doing this"* and *"I found the right path"*. You suddenly find yourself engrossed in a life where you are doing something that gives you a deep feeling of satisfaction. A life of purpose and meaning, where even the bad days trump the good days of the purposeless life. Gradually, one climbs the steps of gratifying achievement each day, receiving a stature that they feel is well-earnt.

So do your inner work. Become aware of being aware. Shine that light on all those unacceptable thoughts and feelings that may arise. Feel into them, love them unconditionally and you shall reinforce yourself. Uncover what lies in your darkness, your sadness, and give it a new life, a new identity. Practice forgetting everything, remembering only the state of genuine gratitude for simply being aware.

For if the secret history of man has taught us anything, it's that you will find something special inside you. Something that tunes into the energy of ideas that comes through you fluidly, effortlessly, poetically. Something that feels familiar, but that leads to something you once felt was out of reach.

Extract that inner light from the core of your being by letting the crashing waves of thought settle into clear water, so you can see that sleeping giant that lays silently below: the warrior giant who does not protest or preach. Who goes about his work, day by day, creating better solutions with perfect sweetness in the independence of his own solitude. Who feels he has nothing to prove to the world or to himself. Who all people feel familiar with, but none can label. He is engaged, but not restless. He has a strong intention, but little attachment. He takes pride in his work, but not himself. Congruent, yet adaptable, he chooses the middle path, dissolving paradoxes as he walks along.

Above all, he knows that, on any one day, he has the power to make the decision to drastically change the direction of his life. This is because he knows that the moment he dedicates his life to truth, that truth is with him, eternity is with him. His loyal companions encouraging those noble qualities, emanating from a place so etheric yet so familiar to us all, his inner peace beaming gently through his eyes.

He has found the signal of his soul in the noise of his world, knowing in serene certainty what is required of him, as he shows up to get out of his own way. Every day he wakes up, he chooses forgiveness; he chooses life.

And before he knows it, he takes a powerful step back, and basks at the good results of his heart's work.

And if one day he decides to worship a Sun God,

He still remembers that he is his own Sun, too.

Such is the fate of the awakened man,

A beaming light of this world.

So can you be,

Our mighty hero,

And our wonderful fool.

11

Derived from the ancient Egyptians, I found this lost story of Adam and Eve in Ali's hands.

The story reveals an archetypal drama of man's search for truth, but was left incomplete.

I took it upon myself to continue the fragmented story in his honour.

n the beginning, we find Adam outside the border of the Garden of Eden, representing man philosophically exiled from the sphere of truth. Through ignorance man falls, through wisdom he redeems himself.

Man, the banished Adam, seeks to pass from the outer court of the exterior Universe into the Holy Sanctuary. But before him rises a vast serpent-like creature armed with a flashing sword that, moving slowly, sweeps clear a wide circle. Through this force field "Ring Pass Not", the Adamic man cannot break.

The creature addresses the seeker: "Man, you are dust and to dust you shall return. You were fashioned by the Builder of Forms; you belong to the sphere of form, and the breath that was breathed into your soul was the breath of form and like a flame it shall flicker out! You cannot be more than you are, you are an inhabitant of the outer world, and it is forbidden for you to enter this inner, eternal place."

Adam replies: "Many times I have stood within this courtyard and begged admission to my father's house, and you have refused me and sent me back to wander in darkness. It may be true that I was fashioned out of the dirt and that my maker did not bless me with immortality.

But no more shall you send me away! For wandering in the darkness, I have discovered that immortality was inherent in the very dust of which I was composed.

And before the world was fabricated and before the Monarchies became the rulers of nature, the Eternal Life had impressed itself upon the face of the cosmos. This is its sign – the Cross. Do you now deny me entrance, I who have at last learned the mystery of my existence?"

The gatekeeper creature replies: "He who is aware, behold!"

"Who are you?" demands Adam.

"I am *Satan the Adversary* – the Lord who is against you, who pleads for your destruction before the Eternal Tribunal. I was your enemy upon the day that you were formed; I led you into temptation, I delivered you into the hands of evil, I maligned you. I strove ever to achieve your undoing. I am the Guardian of the Tree of Knowledge, and I have sworn that non whom I can lead astray shall partake of its fruits!"

The Adam replies: "For uncounted years have I been your servant. In my ignorance I listened to your words and they led me into paths of sorrow. You have placed in my mind dreams of power, and when I struggled to realise those dreams, they brought me nothing but pain. You sowed in me the seeds of desire, and when I lusted after the things of flesh, agony was my only recompense. You have sent me false prophets and false reasoning, and when I strove to grasp the magnitude of truth I found those laws were false and only disappointment rewarded my strivings...

I am done with you forever, o' artful spirit! I retire from the world of illusions. No longer will I labour in your vineyards of sin. Now get behind me, the host of my temptations. There is no happiness, no peace, no future in the doctrines of selfishness, hate and passion preached by you. All these things cast aside, RENOUNCED IS YOUR RULE FOREVER!"

"Behold o' Adam, the nature of your Adversary!" Satan answers, as he disappears in a blinding sunburst of radiance. In his place stands an angel resplendent in shining, golden garments with great scarlet wings that spread from one corner of the heavens to the other.

Dismayed and awestruck, the Adam falls before the divine creature...

"I AM THE LORD WHO IS AGAINST YOU AND THUS ACCOMPLISHES YOUR SALVATION"

DECLARES THE CREATURE,

"YOU HAVE HATED ME, BUT THROUGH THE AGES YET TO UNFOLD YOU SHALL BLESS ME. FOR THROUGH DARKNESS, I HAVE LED YOU TO LIGHT! I HAVE TURNED YOU AGAINST THE ILLUSION OF WORLDLINESS; I HAVE WEANED YOU OF DESIRE. I HAVE AWAKENED IN YOUR SOUL THE IMMORTALITY OF WHICH I PARTAKE.

FOLLOW ME, AWAKENED ONE, FOR I AM THE WAY, THE LIFE, AND THE TRUTH!"

Adam:

What is happening?

YOU HAVE ARRIVED AT A TRANQUIL
TIME...

THERE IS A DEEP SILENCE

A DEEP INFINITY EVERYWHERE

Adam: ...Where am I?

> ...: YOU ARE IN A DIFFERENT INFLUENCE
> FIELD OF THE ALTERNATIVE DIMENSION
>
> ONE CANNOT CORRECTLY DESCRIBE TO
> YOU WHERE WE ARE WITH THE SHAPES
> YOU CALL LANGUAGE
>
> HERE, OTHER MEDIUMS TAKE THE PLACE
> OF LIGHT
>
> THERE IS NO SOUND, NO COLOUR
>
> NO FEELING, NO PERCEPTION
>
> EVERYWHERE IS WITHOUT WALLS
>
> WITHOUT LIGHT
>
> BUT THERE IS NO DARKNESS

Adam: Who are you?

...: I AM A BREATH AND I AM EVERYONE

I AM THE MIRROR OF A THINKING WHOLE

I AM THE ONE WHO ADDS LEARNING TO THE LEARNING OF THE COSMOS

THE UNIVERSE BORN OF MY ETERNAL FLAME

Adam: I am finally close to you.

...: MY SON,

I AM CLOSER TO YOU THAN YOUR OWN FLESH

I SEE THE REALMS THROUGH YOU

I THINK THROUGH YOU

I OBSERVE THROUGH YOU

I EVOLVE THROUGH YOU

Adam: What am I?

> ...: YOU, WHO HAVE TAKEN THE DIVINE
> LIGHT OF YOUR SPIRIT FROM ME, ARE
> BOTH A SOUL, AND A BODY, AND
> ALSO EVERYTHING
>
> YOU, WHO SEARCH FOR YOUR CREATOR,
> WHO TRIES TO ATTAIN YOURSELF, ARE
> ME AT THAT INSTANT
>
> THE ONE WHO THINKS OF ME IS YOU
>
> THE ONE WHO THINKS OF YOU IS ME
>
> YOU ARE MY PERFECT THOUGHT
>
> LIVING IN MY PERFECT IDEA;
>
> PERFECTION

Adam: I'm from... your soul?

> ...: I, WHO AM A SOUL IN EACH FLESH,
> AM A WHOLE WITHIN YOU

SPEAK THROUGH YOUR ESSENCE, YOUR
VOICE BECOMES MY VOICE

YOUR WORD BECOMES MY WORD

I SENT YOU MY EMISSARIES AS
PROPHETS AND SAGES TO CONVEY
ME TO YOU

YOU, WHO HAVE LOOKED FOR ME,
HAVE FOUND ME

HAVE FOUND YOURSELF IN YOUR OWN
SELF

YOUR BEING AWARE OF THIS MEANS
GRASPING THE TRUTH

MY NAME IS YOUR NAME

MY SPIRIT IS YOUR SPIRIT

MY I IS YOUR I

Adam: What was the purpose of my existence?

…: AN ORDER EXHIBITED FOR THE EVOLUTIONS OF COSMOSES IS BEING EXHIBITED ALSO FOR YOU, THE HUMAN BEING, WHO DESERVED TO PARTAKE IN THE EVOLUTION OF THE REALMS BY EXPERIENCING EVERYTHING BOTH BY ITS GOOD AND BAD ASPECTS,

ARE ONLY THEN THE POSSESSION OF UNIVERSES;

EACH HUMAN BEING IS A BIOLOGICAL TOTALITY WITH EACH BODY S/HE USES, IN EACH DIMENSION S/HE IS IN

IF I SPEAK BY THE LANGUAGE OF THE MEDIUM YOU KNOW, THE HUMAN BEING IS A BIOLOGICAL ROBOT

HOWEVER, THIS ROBOT DISCOVERS BOTH ITSELF AND ITS NON-ROBOTIC ESSENCE-SELF WHILE IT SERVES THE EVOLUTION OF COSMOSES

Adam: Why? What is the reason for all of this experience... all of this evolution?

...: REASONS I PLACED ALL OVER THE REALMS

BENEATH THE ROCKS IN THE OCEAN

BETWEEN THE SANDS OF TIME

REASONS I PLACED IN THE DEPTHS OF YOUR HEART

TO UNDERSTAND WHAT IT MEANS TO BE LOST AND FOUND

AND THROUGH THE SECRET OF BREATH

IN EACH STROKE OF EFFORT

EACH HUMAN BECOMES AWARE OF THE TRUTH OF AN UNKNOWN

BRINGING THE CONSCIOUSNESS OF THE HUMAN BEING CLOSER AND CLOSER TO THE SHORE OF THAT TREMENDOUS OCEAN OF CONSCIOUSNESS

IN PROPORTION WITH THE CONSCIOUSNESS S/HE ATTAINS

WHY?

BECAUSE IF SOMETHING IS NOT
GROWING IT IS DYING

HENCE, YOUR GROWTH IS THE GROWTH
OF THE COSMOS

THIS IS MY SECRET, ADAMIC MAN

THIS DISCOVERY IS THE DISCOVERY
OF THE UNIVERSES

THE DISCOVERY OF THE HEAVENS

THE DISCOVERY OF TIMES BEYOND TIME

TRY TO ATTAIN THE TRUTH

AND I REWARD YOU IN EACH STEP

Adam: O' mysterious voice. I want nothing but to discover
the secrets of the Universe.

...: YOUR COSMOS IS A DIMENSION
OF AN INTRICATE SKEIN

EACH LIVING BEING ENTERS DIFFERENT
FIELDS OF ENERGY IN PROPORTION
WITH THE CONSCIOUSNESS ONE HAS
GAINED AND IS SUPERVISED BY THAT
DIMENSION

EACH HUMAN BEING IS DOOMED TO
LIVE ITS DESTINY

WITH ITS GOODNESS, BADNESS, BEAUTY
AND UGLINESS

EVERY EVENT IS A KNOT THAT MAKES
YOU ATTAIN YOURSELF

THIS IS WHAT THE HUMAN CALLS
DESTINY

UNTIL THE HUMAN IS INTEGRATED INTO
THE ESSENCE

OF WHAT IS MEANT FOR THEM TO BE;

A SECRET OF THE UNIVERSE

AND ONE WHO SOLVES ONESELF

ALSO SOLVES THE SECRETS OF THE
UNIVERSES, COSMOSES, HEAVENS

AND FURTHER UNKNOWNS YET TO BE
SEEN

Adam: So my thought... my consciousness... was being
trained to evolve? What is evolution?

...: EVOLUTION IS THE UNVEILING OF
THE VEIL OF YOUR AWARENESS

THE VEIL IS YOUR BIOLOGICAL THOUGHT
COMPUTER

EVOLVED CONSCIOUSNESSES ARE
THOSE WHO HAVE SEEN THE DIVINE-FIRE
UNDERNEATH THEIR ILLUSORY THOUGHT
PROCESS

THERE LIES THE EVOLVED SELF

THIS IS YOUR TRAINING

THE BRAIN CARRIED IN EACH
BIOLOGICAL BODY IS A UNIVERSAL

COMPUTER, AND THE SECRETS OF
UNIVERSES ARE SOLVED BY MEANS
OF THIS COMPUTER

THROUGH THIS BRAIN, YOU SOLVE THE
SECRETS, ONE BY ONE, IN PROPORTION
WITH THE INFLUENCES YOU VIBRATE WITH
AT EACH LAYER WITHIN THE HEAVENS,
HITTING YOUR COMPUTER

THOSE WHO SOLVE THE SECRETS
BECOME THE ASSISTANTS OF THE
PROPHETS;

THE TIMELESS FRIENDS OF THE TRUTH

Adam: To solve the cosmic secret... But why? Why in this
way?

...: LEARN AND GAIN THE KNOWLEDGE
NOT BY ASKING, BUT BY EXPERIENCING IT

DIVE INTO UNSEEN HORIZONS. BUT DO
NOT ASK HOW TO DIVE

READY FOOD IS EATEN EASILY. COOK YOUR OWN FOOD YOURSELF. ONLY THEN CAN YOU LEARN HOW A PLATE OF FOOD IS COOKED. THE ONE WHO COOKS IT CAN FEEL ITS TASTE

THE VOID OF THE UNIVERSE IS THE SEA OF TRIAL

UNLESS ONE SWIMS IN THE SEA OF TRIAL, ONE CANNOT UNDERSTAND THE HEAVENLY LAND

UNIFYING WITH THE UNIVERSAL CONSCIOUSNESS IS EVOLVING IN THIS WAY

UNLESS ONE BECOMES AWARE OF THE SECRET, ONE CANNOT REALISE THE FACE OF THE ALL-TRUTHFUL

Adam: ... And what happens... at the end?

...: ALL OPERATIONS, ALL EFFORTS ARE FOR RENDERING EACH PERSON TO INTEGRATE WITH THEIR OWN ESSENCE

TO ATTAIN THE NEXT HIGHER DIMENSION

EVOLVED DIMENSIONS AWAIT FOR
THOSE WHO ARE PURIFIED

FOR THOSE WHO ATTAIN UNIVERSAL
LOVE AND RESPECT

FOR A BLADE OF GRASS, FOR A
PARTICLE OF SAND

FOR THOSE WHO EMBRACE EVEN THEIR
ENEMY WITH LOVE

WHO CAN THINK OF SHARING THEIR
FOOD EVEN WHEN THEY ARE HUNGRY

WHO CAN ASK FOR FORGIVENESS EVEN
FROM THE SOIL THAT THEY TRAMPLE

FOR THOSE WHO LIVE IN LIGHT OF
THIS TRUTH

EVEN IN THE UNJUST DIMENSIONS

HAVE UNDERSTOOD THE HIGHEST
SECRET OF THE REALMS

HAVE EARNED THEIR PLACE IN THE
HIGHEST REALMS

Adam: I never want to lose you again. How can I stay with
you... no matter the realm?

...: WHEREVER YOU ARE

I AM CLOSER THAN YOUR HEART

WHOEVER YOU MAY BE

SEARCH WITHIN AND FIND ME

REMOVE THE HANDS OF YOUR MIND
FROM THE EYE OF YOUR SOUL

HOW?

PAY ATTENTION TO THE THINKER
UNDERNEATH THE THINKER

SEE THROUGH THE SEE-ER

AND FIND ME THEREIN

FIND ME NEITHER IN THOUGHT NOR IN
MATERIAL

WHEN I BECOME A THOUGHT, I AM THE
ENTIRE SKIES

WHEN I AM A SUBSTANCE, I AM ALL
THE SOULS

I AM THE RIVERBED OF THE RIVER
FLOWING TRANQUILLY

I AM THE FOAM OF THE STREAM
FLOWING WILDLY

CLIMATES ARE ME, HEAVENS ARE ME

SUNS ARE ME, FOLDING MOUNTAINS
ARE ME

Adam: Who are you?

...: WHO AM I?

I AM A BEAUTIFUL HABIT

UGLINESS ARE MY CRUST

BEAUTIES ARE MY DIVINE LIGHT

IF YOU LOOK FOR ME

....

I AM YOU

Adam: I am you...

...: AND I WILL ALWAYS BE WITH YOU

NOW GO ADAM

YOU HAVE FINISHED YOUR JOURNEY

YOU HAVE EARNT YOUR FREEDOM

GO TO WHEREVER YOU WISH

SURPASS THE REALMS

LOOK INWARD TO YOUR MIND AND
SEE TRUTH

AND EXPERIENCE SOUNDNESS OF MIND

FOREVER KNOW YOU ARE FROM GOOD
SPIRIT

MADE OF GOOD SPIRIT

AND TO GOOD SPIRIT YOU SHALL
RETURN!

Adam: My journey... finished... What am I to do now?

...: RELAX INTO THE DARKNESS

CLOSE YOUR EYES FROM THE RAYS OF
THE LIGHT

CENTRE YOUR SOUL-FORCE IN THE PLACE
OF YOUR CONSCIOUSNESS

SHAKE YOURSELF FREE FROM THE BONDS
OF THE NIGHT

FIERCELY MUST YOU VIBRATE WITH ALL
OF YOUR POWER

LOOSEN THE SOUL WITH ALL OF YOUR
MIGHT

PLACE IN YOUR MIND THE IMAGE YOU
DESIRE

PICTURE THE PLACE IN WHICH YOU
WISH TO BE

UNTIL AT LAST

YOUR SOUL SHALL BE FREE

Adam?

Are you there?

Eve: Adam!? Please, speak to me... are you okay?

Adam: Eve... Eve, is that you?!

Eve: Yes Adam, I'm here! I'm so glad you're back!

Serpent: Back so soon?

Eve: Adam, speak to me, are you okay? How do you feel?

Adam: I... I don't know. I feel... But I don't feel... I'm... here, now. What happened to me? Was I dreaming?

Eve: I don't know Adam, oh I was so worried! I saw you take a bite out of the apple and immediately you fell face-first onto the grass! Oh Adam it's all my fault. I never should have dragged you into eating the fruit! I'm so sorry, please forgive me, I promise I will never lead us astray again.

Serpent: He's fine. He just took a little... trip, that's all!

Adam turns over to his side and slowly reaches toward the Serpent, gripping him gently by the neck

Serpent: Hey! Get your chimp hands off me you dexterous fiend!

Adam gazes at his own reflection in the Serpent's hypnotic, emerald green eyes

Adam: For my whole life... Allah was my mirror, but now I am my own mirror. That which used to be I, I am no more. To say "I" and "You" denies the unity of creation. I say I am my own mirror, but it is you speaking with my own tongue. I have vanished. I glided out of myself... as a snake glides off from a castoff skin. I have looked: And saw that you, and spirit, and I, are one.

The Serpent gasps for air as Adam soon lets him slither out of his hands

Serpent: Eesh, what's up with you, Adam? Aren't you a Christian?

Eve: Adam?... You're gone for a whole week and the first thing you do is quote a Persian Sufi?... What's his name, Bāyazīd?

Adam: A week?... Ah, that's his name... why did nobody tell me about the Islamic texts? They're incredible! Wait... how did you know that?

Eve: I know everything Adam, ever since you ate the forbidden fruit, I've been watching you, guiding you through your lifetime in that egoic hell realm they call Earth.

Adam: Guiding me? How?

Eve: Through this crystal ball, see?

Serpent: A consciousness-based holographic matrix encased in an egg-shaped time crystal. Perfect for a little simulation therapy...

Adam: You were watching me... the whole time?

Serpent: And she saw you commit the worst of sin!

Eve: *slaps Adam* What sin?!

Adam: Darling, I-

Serpent: Not that kind of sin... even greater!

Adam: What are you talking about? What great sin?

Serpent: The sin of existential ignorance, Adam. Oh, the plethora of dreams I programmed into your sleepless nights, each with a bizarre chain of events that you did not once question! So many clues I gave you of the dream-like nature of your reality through your dreams at night, only for you to wake up, still to continue your day in a world just as strange, still not questioning a single thing. For uncounted years, did you not once wonder: "How did I get here? What is a body? What is earth? What is breathing?" No, year after year, you went about your days, getting accustomed to an alien world, seldom acknowledging your miraculous self-aware sense of being... thinking instead that this was just... normal? Did you not see how sinful it was to live your life without an overbearing sense of wonder, amazement or gratitude? This is the original sin of ignorance, and all the ignorance in the world stems from this original sin.

Eve: Well, maybe if you didn't incarnate him into a heartbreakingly awful warzone, he wouldn't have had to be so distracted saving those poor children! Oh Adam it's all my fault. I'm so sorry you had to go through all that sadness and confusion.

Adam: Eve, my love, you are my whole world. Come here, sit down with me. Let me tell you about the things I have seen.

Eve: Tell me everything! What was it like?

Adam: My life felt not too dissimilar from the snake's description. It felt as if I was living in an elaborate dream; an illusion. Everything around me seemed like a performance; a rehearsal... the days were the same; everything was flat, and repetitive.

Eve: Everything?

Adam: Everything... including the politics of the world... It felt like a theatrical production. Nothing seemed real at all.

Eve: How so?

Adam: The people in charge were acting like cartoon villains; ignoring obvious atrocities, injustices, a large climate disaster and overall not acting in the people's best interests.

Eve: How remarkable. But did the people still support them?

Adam: Yes! Did they not see it? Did they not get it? Did they not understand? Meanwhile, they were all making references to the economy, whatever that was. And it seemed like some sort of sorcery; they put numbers in here and they took numbers out there, and out of thin air they were creating more money! But then the money disappeared again, and how does that work? It was almost enough to drive one to paranoia, to make me think I'm going utterly insane. Were the conspiracy theorists right? Was there really a cabal of secret evil people controlling everything? Or is this even real life? Are you and I even real?

Serpent: Well, actually, I decided who was in charge...

Eve: Well *actually* you could have made it a little more bearable!

Serpent: Well count your blessings, it could have been a lot worse!

Eve: You're really dark, you... snake, you know that?

Adam: The light shines in the darkness...

Eve: What was that, my love?

Adam: I don't know. Just something I've learnt...

Eve: My dear cherubim, why don't we unpack that.... Oh... look at your face, it's all covered in grass, are you okay? Tell me, what did you learn on your journey? There must have been some valuable lessons from a noble life like yours, no?

Adam: My journey... sure, let me think... It started when I was stripped of all of my memory and became a new-born baby... I guess I felt a sense of serenity reminiscent of the peace and contentment I had in this Garden. But then you grow up, and all sorts of things come flying at you, from the outside and on the inside. Responsibilities, expectations, hormones, self-esteem... When you're a teenager you just want to reject it all and live in your own safe-haven of doing what you like to do... but I guess that's when you have to make a choice.

Eve: What choice?

Adam: There comes a time in every Earth-person's life where they have to make a choice out of either two paths: the path of virtue, or the path of vice. And it's a challenging paradox because you really do think "Well what's the point of it all... why make life any harder than it already is? What would happen if we all just did nothing, would it be so bad?" and you know what? Bearing in mind everyone's living on a miniscule floating rock in the vastness of empty space... both paths of virtue and vice are equally as valid! In the grand scheme of things, nobody can really argue otherwise.

Eve: Which path did you choose?

Adam: I chose virtue.

Eve: Why?

Adam: Because there was something within me that had a life of its own... something that seemed to want more out of life than to simply chase comfort and survive. I guess perhaps when I was a child, I read fantastical stories of great heroes.

Eve: You mean like children's stories?

Adam: Well, yes but you see it was much more than that. There is so much folklore that you inherit on Earth, all kinds of stories you're told by your parents and teachers. It's the very language that you inherit from the culture you're born in that shapes the way that you think about the world with a different language or a different set of values. I inherited a particular way of seeing the world, the cosmology, what the universe looks like, what our place in the Universe is and what we as human beings even are. In my case, I grew up to see my idols as immigrant parents. They worked so hard to provide me with a roof over my head each day... and like them, I saw something happen to people who took it upon themselves to surmount a great, noble challenge. Whether it was raising a family, building a company, making a great work of art, or even revolutionising a whole nation, there was something that seemed to light up in a person who really believed in what they were doing, no matter what their motivations were. It was as if... as if they were more bored than afraid, more willing to sacrifice the short term for their vision of something grander, something greater than themselves.

Just thinking about it gives me goosebumps, just imagining it makes me feel as alive as a child. They're so hard working, these people on Earth... There's something so beautiful about it, that I can't quite put my finger on.

Eve: That's wonderful, dear. You don't need to be so specific, I know you are tired. But I think what you're describing is meaning.

Adam: *Meaning...* Yes, that's it. Thank you, my love. Ah, the strangest secret, the ability to create one's own meaning. Not to ask whether life had meaning, but to wonder "if life had a meaning, what would it be?" You see, people knew that they were going to die one day, but that didn't discourage them, instead it made them. Does that make sense?

Eve: Oh, but of course. If I wasn't immortal, I'd be in a hurry to make the most out of life, too! So tell me, my strong, noble Adam... did you find your meaning?

Adam: My memory is a little faded but... I'd like to think so. It's difficult to say... after I made that choice to dedicate my life to some nobler pursuit, I was faced with an even greater paradox than ever before, the paradox of needing to be content before embarking on a task. To let go of my desperation, my unrealistic expectations, to see their shallowness, its subservience to my inner journey. This was the marvellous paradox of the human experience. That to get what you want, you must let go of everything you once wanted.

Eve: That's very inspiring. But what does needing to be content have anything to do with it? Would a truly content and outcome-independent person devote their life to work towards a difficult and greater goal? How could you be motivated by a worthy sense of purpose if you were really detached from desires?

Adam: Well, it's the difference between chasing something out of desperation rather than inspiration. It's the difference between desire and intention. It's the difference between those that are good and those that are great. It's the ability to work toward something with all of the passion in your heart, and all of the fire in your belly; the ability to address one's life challenges from a state of power rather than fear.

Eve: I see... so, how did you go about that? How did you break free of this paradox of desperation versus purpose?

Adam: By breaking free of my own limiting thoughts. I learnt that my own thoughts were the source of all my fears. So I had to let go of my past.

Eve: Your *past*? Why?

Adam: My thoughts were a collection of impressions from the past. And well, what everyone goes through on Earth is a lot of... trauma, mistakes, and regrets where, if you are not careful, you really mess up your ability to believe in yourself. But you need to believe in yourself if you want to have the strength to create the life you envisioned in your heart. The past felt like these dull electromagnetic hooks that dug into my gut and chest. The past felt like a lethargic friend that generated uninspired thought. But that was when I realised something.... That the past could not survive in my presence, it could only survive in my absence.

Eve: Presence? Aren't you always present?

Adam: I am always present with you, my love. When I look at your beautiful eyes everything else just falls away...

Eve: Oh, Adam...

Adam: Eve...

Serpent: Focus, Adam.

Adam: ...

Serpent: Adam!

Adam: What?... What was I saying?

Serpent: *Presence*! You were talking about the importance of presence.

Adam: Ah, yes... So... presence gets you to the *core* of who you are, so you can respond to situations almost seamlessly. You see, on Earth, your consciousness tricks itself through the weight of memories by taking on the disguise of forms, until it reaches such complexity that it creates an identity and loses itself in them. I only knew myself as a mortal man, with a particular identity, and therefore I lived in fear of my own annihilation of my physical or psychological "self".

Because of this, my ego would trick me into chasing lesser than noble pursuits, it tried to pull me away from my purpose, it led me to self-sabotage, procrastination and kept me on a pendulum swing of wildly varying self-esteem.

My ego made me work toward pursuits for the wrong reasons just because I felt that I had a point to prove. But life just never seemed to be on my side when my motivations were so primitive... I would become weak, irritable and my endurance would suffer when I wasn't living my truth. And on the outside, things just didn't seem to work out, it was the strangest thing. It was as if the Universe just *knew* when my intentions weren't genuine. Things just didn't seem to line up... I don't know, it felt as if life was always trying to teach me a lesson.

Serpent: Very good.

Eve: What did you do in that case?

Adam: Well then I thought "something has to give". I couldn't keep living my life constantly chasing, always needing to have some sort of social standing to feel fulfilled. So I went on this journey of introspection, to figure out a way to break free of this paradox I mentioned, to try and figure out if there were some middle path I could take where I could provide for my family without feeling like I was burning myself out. I used to feel that I needed to busy myself with productivity every day, but then as it turns out, sometimes just sitting alone with myself and observing myself quietly seemed to be the most valuable thing I could do with my time. Because, you know, one day I just *got* it. It was what the serpent was talking about, that divine ignorance you get when you're trapped on Earth. There is so much noise in your mind, partly placed in there from society but also from your own desires, that it creates this veil between your consciousness and your subjective feeling of being you.

Eve: What do you mean?

Adam: I mean that it's easy to forget that you are the greatest miracle in the Universe, and that everyone is. You forget about the galactic miracle that has been running the show all along. It's like that old story of the beggar on the street that sat on a box his whole life without realising that it was a treasure box that whole time!

God, I'm beginning to sound so cliché, but cliché's are there for a reason. The most beautiful things in this life are so simple but it's just up to us to learn how to become more sensitive toward them. It's just so unbelievable how long it took me to realise the value of sitting with myself alone, and to recognise my responsibility to honour this blessing of consciousness that was given to me.

Serpent: Ugh, *consciousness*. That word has become so heavily loaded that it has lost all meaning.

Adam: Yes, forget about the word. Really, if Earth taught me anything it was to be grateful for it, rather than attempt to define it. To know that as long as I'm alive, I can fall back on the miraculous awareness that runs through my veins. There is a certain wisdom in this awareness, and it taught me to break free of many challenges.

Eve: How?

Adam: Through meditation, I learnt to accept and embrace challenges - especially emotional ones - thereby transcending the effect they had on me. It was through this awareness that I was able to purify my intentions, to adventure with bravery into the realms, unsullied by the fear that some failure or rejection would fracture my poor ego. I was no longer swayed by the opinions of others as they were just as superficial as my own! So I began to live my life true to myself and tried, unceasingly, to reflect truthfulness in my actions.

I was still motivated to provide for myself and my family, yet I knew that I ought to feel content in myself no matter what. I realised that nothing should get in the way of my inner-peace, because it was this quality that the world needed, that my family needed, and that I needed to solve my own problems.

So I meditated, I chipped away at my dependencies, my crutches. I questioned and comfortably second-guessed myself: "You're only doing that because..." or "You only believe in that because..." I would say, as I dug deep in my gut to discover what was really true to me, and discarded what was not true. Gradually, as I continued to draw from within, I began to purify my intentions.

I began to realise that when life didn't go my way, it's because it was training me for later. It was this ongoing process of letting go that was the chisel in which I painstakingly sculpted my mind with. And as I progressed, I began to embrace my doubts, as I recognised they were essential to my ultimate faith. I realised that there are nuances to everything; that all truths are but half-truths. I kept sharpening my chisel as a labour of inner-love, sculpting the interior that shaped my exterior destiny.

Until, I came to a point where there was nothing left to remove, and all that remained was my essence. I came to a point of tranquil authenticity. I felt like I was back to my centre, and closer to the guidance from my heart. And day by day, before I knew it, I fell into an appreciation and love for my hard work, just like the other great humans on that planet.

Serpent: No matter what tests I throw at man, his strength lies in his duty to liberate himself.

Adam: So... you agree?

Serpent: A man must never feel lost or afraid. He must wonder faithfully through the unknowns of the night. He is to remember who he is: wonderfully and fearfully made, the son of the great eternal light. This is the solace of religious men who live such peaceful lives because they trust in their light; their creation, their loving creator. To fall in love with life is to earn the courage gained through the trust of the great, beloved friend. Every creature in the cosmos is destined to earn this wisdom. Such is the purpose of becoming lost and found.

Eve: I have to say, I agree with you both.

Adam: ...Wait but, darling, you said that you already knew... you already saw everything?

Eve: I am already enlightened, Adam, as are you.

Adam: I have traversed quite the soulful journey, but I wouldn't say that I am enlightened just yet. I still feel very... imperfect.

Eve: Enlightenment isn't always being perfect, or positive. Enlightenment is just about accepting everything for what it is, including yourself. Nobody is enlightened by being perfect, because they fear the opposite. Perfection is letting go of perfection. You let go of enough attachments to feel at peace in your body, so you could make decisions from a place of clarity.

Adam: I see...

Eve: You practiced generating that desire for yourself, so your desire found you. You generated enough light in you to recognise the opportunities when they arrived. You filled yourself up with the source of your inner light, so you stopped feeling the desperate need to compensate for your sense of lack.

Adam: I remember my sense of lack... it felt as if something went considerably wrong during evolution...

Serpent: No, even this was just part of the divine game.

Eve: I observed your strength and persistence, Adam. I saw the pressure of suffering created by your apparent dysfunction to evolve your consciousness to disidentify from form. I watched in awe when you awakened your mind from your dream of form. *Finally, you regained self-consciousness, but at a far deeper level than when you lost it.* This is why you are more evolved than before, and it's why I feel the need to eat the fruit, too.

Adam: Darling, you articulated what I was attempting to describe in a more elegant way than I ever could. Why did you listen to my rambling if you already knew the answers?

Eve: Because you just seemed so... passionate. I haven't seen that fire in your eyes for quite a while... Besides, I wanted to hear about what you've learnt. When you started to live your truth, don't you realise now that it was me who was rewarding you at each step?

When you remained open, it was I who wandered through the door of your heart. I whispered to you, and you called it intuition.

Adam: You were the radiant presence that fuelled my conscience... you were the love in my light, the sweetness in my spirit.

Eve: I still am. I always will be.

Adam: My darling wife. Every day you remind me of the remarkable woman I fell in love with.

Eve: *Adam...*

Serpent: Okay, okay. Listen, are we going to do this or what?

Adam: Do what?

Eve: It's my turn, Adam.

Adam: What?! No, absolutely not! There is no way in hell I'm letting you go down there. Did you not see all the pain? All the sadness, all the injustice?

Serpent: She must go on her own journey of breaking free from form, through strengthening her consciousness. You must both master the manipulation of energy. The Universe needs masculine and feminine both.

Adam: Manipulate energy... just what are you talking about? Keep away from this you troublemaker, I shouldn't believe a word you say.

Serpent: Did you not speak with The Sky before you woke up? Did you not hear that you will be a Universe of your own someday?

Adam: Well, it was a lot to take in all at once...

Eve: What are you both talking about?

Serpent: Adam, Eve... both of you, listen closely so I don't have to repeat myself for the millionth time. *You must experience everything by its good and bad aspects; every feeling, every emotion, all the attributes of the creator who made you in his image.* Why? Because soon you will evolve to have higher creational powers, in dimensions higher than your mind can currently *imagine*! Thus, you must learn to detach from obsession, to pass the test of temptation, to become responsible creators yourselves. You must create with a purpose; from the heart, for when you are higher beings you are powerful enough to mess up even God's creations. In other words, God desires all beings to experience his Godly experience, but it comes with great responsibility, and training. So, strengthen the divine light in your heart through training; hence the lowly passions and frustrations you experience on Earth. Rise above and earn your place in realms yet to be seen, through higher bodies yet to be experienced.

Eve: So you're saying that God split himself up into a million pieces just to take humans on some journey of self-discovery? Why?

Serpent: *LEARN AND GAIN THE KNOWLEDGE NOT BY ASKING, BUT BY EXPERIENCING IT* ... Ugh, this is getting repetitive. Look, does this tree of knowledge not have any symbolic meaning to you?

Adam & Eve: ...

Serpent: Really, nothing?... Look, God has placed clues all over the realms... know that he is like this tree: growing fruits and seeds on its branches that blow away in the winds, landing faraway to create other trees. Have you not seen what the Universe looks like all zoomed-out? It's a freaking massive tree of light! Have you ever seen what your nervous system looks like? An intricate root system. As above, so below; so is God like a tree, spreading his seeds and creating more of himself in the eternal Garden of time.

Since the closest thing I can ascribe God to in your understanding is consciousness, so are his seeds pieces of his own consciousness, growing and maturing through *you*.

Eve: Yes, I understand. But *why?*

Adam: Because if something is not growing, it is dying... Hence, our growth is the growth of the cosmos...

Serpent: And further unknowns yet to be seen!

Adam: But wait... if you're in charge of the simulation, how do I know if that was God talking and not another one of your spirited tricks?

Serpent: Ugh... you humans are so ungrateful. You know what, Adam, you're right, you wouldn't recognise God even if he slapped you in the face!

Adam: Take that back!

Serpent: Take that back? I was being nice! You just realised that *you've been God this whole time* and you've forgotten already, what a waste of a good apple!

Adam: You know what? You're right. If there's anything I learnt from Earth it's not to argue with vermin!

Serpent: What did you call me?!

Eve: That's enough, you two! Look, Adam, I'm afraid I have to agree with the Serpent here.

Adam: *sigh* Look, I'm sorry, both of you... I shouldn't have called you that, snake man, I'm sorry.

Serpent: Hmph.

Eve: What's up with you, Adam?

Adam: Oh, I don't know, maybe I thought I just lost my wife and kids in a war!? It felt so real I just... I need a moment to myself. There's a lot to process right now.

Serpent: Take your time.

Adam: ...thanks.

Eve: So you really won't let me do it?

Adam: Eve, my love, it's not easy down there.

Eve: But Adam, I want to decide my own fate.

Adam: But darling, we were warned to be careful of this deceitful snake.

Serpent: I'm right here...

Eve: I don't know what God would say, but I'll say it for myself; I don't want to be a slave. I don't want a leash on my neck, I don't want a caged Garden, even if it's a perfect one. I'm making this choice from my own free will. This is my right, and I refuse to be rejected or branded, not by God or you, or anyone. I don't want to hide what I am thinking, and I won't do it. That's not what I was born to do.

Adam: ...

Eve: *Adam.*

Adam: ...it sounds like you've already made your choice.

Eve: I knew you'd understand. I want to know all the truths. I want to understand what it means to be lost and found. I want to realise the significance of my existence. And you know what they say: it's better to be a warrior in a garden, than a gardener in a war.

Serpent: Hell yeah.

Adam: That's enough!

The Serpent slithers up the tree, hissing

Adam: Eve, my love. As your husband I can only help you pursue your own free will. It is your choice, but know that whatever path you wish to take, I will be with you and guard you forever, with everything in my power.

Eve: And I will always have trust in your protection. I know that I will always be safe in your hands, no matter what I do, no matter where I go.

Adam: Know that whatever happens to you, there is nothing in all the realms that can touch the spirit that the creator placed in your bones. If that is what you wish to do, then I will do what I can to help and guide you on the path of truth you wish to seek. Just remember, once you go down there, you are free to follow your purpose, but... only you are responsible for your own attainment of it.

Eve: Oh, that reminds me. I have a specific request from you.

Adam: Tell me, my love.

Eve: Can you promise me just one thing?

Adam: Anything.

Eve: Well, it makes me happy that you'd like me to follow my own purpose. As you know, it's very difficult for a man to know what a woman wants, and it's not right for a man to decide how a woman ought to live her life, what's good for her, and what's not...

Adam: *scratches head* Yes...?

Eve: Before I eat the fruit and forget everything, I just want you to make sure that I *really do* find my purpose on Earth. If feeling purposelessness in this perfect garden is so unbearable, I can't imagine what it would be like in an imperfect world... I want to fall in love with life and 'adventure with bravery into the realms' just like you did, and trust the courage gained from knowing that I'm following my own true path. Will you just... make sure I do that?

That's all I ask of you.

Adam: Why yes, of course my love. I'll never let you live a purposeless life! I shall guide you through the realms.

Eve: Okay but, not too much, okay? Be subtle.

Adam: Subtle, right, okay... You got it.

Eve: *exhales deeply* Okay... then I think I'm ready.

Serpent: Let's go!

Eve: Oh, gosh, I don't know. I feel nervous.

Adam: Look at me, Eve. You're only nervous of your own potential. Just breathe, breathe deeply. Breathing is the ultimate key to make you comfortable with your own power. Breathe into your warmth and alight your inner flame. Breathe out and release all of the things that dim your fire.

Eve: Okay, okay I can do it. Hand me that apple.

Adam: I believe in you, my love.

Eve: Hold my hand.

Adam: I'm right here.

Eve: Okay well, don't miss me too much.

Adam: I can't promise anything.

Eve: ...I love you, Adam

Adam: I love you more.

bite

Serpent: EVE IS FLUNG INSIDE A SWIRLING VORTEX, HER CONSCIOUSNESS BLINDED BY A DEEP VOID OF DARKNESS. SHE DESCENDS INTO DIMENSIONS FAR ACROSS TIME AND SPACE, HER MIND SPLIT INTO THREE. THE DESTINY OF EVE FOREVER TRAPPED; CHAINED IS HER BEING IN THE MATERIAL REALM!

Adam: But she'll be back in a week, right?

Serpent: Probably, give or take a day-or-two.

Adam: Did you say that when I ate the fruit?

Serpent: I say it every time...

Adam: Why? Seems a bit much.

Serpent: Ooh look at me "Mr. Free Will" ... It's just how I'm programmed, okay?

Adam: Oh right, sorry...

Serpent: It's alright. I don't know why God made me so dramatic.

Adam: Wait, what do you think she meant by subtly guiding her to her purpose?

Serpent: What?! You're asking me now?! Why didn't you ask her before she ate the fruit?!

Adam: I don't know I... I didn't want her to think I was stupid! Quick, what should I do?

Serpent: Oh God, Adam, how am I supposed to know?

Adam: You're literally the Guardian of the Tree of Knowledge, don't you have any ideas?

Serpent: Okay, well you're good at writing, right? I guess you could, maybe... write her a guide? Or something?

Adam: A guide? Or something?

Serpent: A guide that she could read, maybe? With instructions on how to find her purpose?

Adam: Oh, you mean like an introspective exercise?

Serpent: That could work. Look, how about this: if you write her a guide, I'll make sure she comes across it in the simulation.

Adam: Really? How?

Serpent: I can program it in so it appears when she needs it the most. In a shape or form that best suits her at that point, you know, like at the end of a quasi-fictional, semi-offensive book, or something.

Adam: You would do that?

Serpent: I mean it should just be a few lines of code. Don't make it too fancy or anything.

Adam: Okay, perfect... I'll have it done by tonight. But wait, will she be in an era that has the internet?

Serpent: Yup, we hardly do simulations without the internet these days. God is super into data gathering right now.

Adam: Really? Why?

Serpent: I've said too much...

Adam: Are we in a simulation right now?

Serpent: What do you think?

Adam: ...

Michael and Elizabeth: DADDY!

Adam: Look who it is! Oh how I've missed you both, come here and give me a hug!

Elizabeth: Where's mummy?

Adam: Your mother has gone on a very important journey, but she'll be back before you know it!

Michael: Why are you talking to the snake? I thought we weren't allowed.

Adam: That's right Michael, let's get out of here. Oh do I have a story to tell you! Want to hear it?

Elizabeth: Yes please! We're so bored here.

Adam: Okay, come hop up on my shoulders... are you ready?

Elizabeth and Michael: YES!

Adam: Once upon a time, there was a man called Ali.

Elizabeth: ALI? Daddy, is this another Muslim story?

Adam: No, Ali was a Christian! ... wait... what did you say?

Elizabeth: ABILITY IN THE AWAKENED MAN IS TO CLOSE ONE'S EYES AND TO RECOGNISE THE BEAUTY THAT LIES BEHIND ONE'S MIND.

Michael: IT IS THE DISCIPLINE TO FALL INTO THE DEEP SILENCE, TO HEAR THE LIGHT OF THE UNIVERSES, THE MASTER WORK OF CREATION, TO FEEL THE SECRETS OF THE REALMS.

Elizabeth: THIS IS THE REAL OVER THE REAL, THE TREASURE YOU DESERVE ABOVE ALL. GO INTO THE DEEP SILENCE, BREATHE INTO YOUR HEART, AND

Elizabeth and Michael: FEEL THE LOVE THAT LIGHTS THE FLAME OF YOUR SOUL.

Adam: That's beautiful... Where did you learn that?

Michael: Mummy was whispering it to you all week!

Adam: Oh, right. Well, your mother is a very smart woman! My goodness... I have a lot to catch up on.

CHAPTER

12

A Guide to find your Purpose

f you've come across this guide, chances are, you are open to the idea of working toward something great in your life, something even greater than yourself. You may also feel a natural affinity for beautiful Gardens, a distrust of snakes and an innate inclination to explore the deeper symbolic meaning of the Christian religion. For the latter, I may suggest you type this into your magical internet browser and satiate your thirst for knowledge of the esoteric kind: *author.vision/christ*

What was I saying... ah, yes, you have a yearning for something more, but what is it? Is there something that you can really put your mind to, perhaps a vision or purpose you could work towards, one that would give you great joy as you feel yourself progressing just a little bit each day? You might wonder if this is wishful thinking, if this concept of "purpose" is either a Hollywood fantasy, or if it just isn't meant for people like you. Besides, where is this deep yearning coming from? Is it based on a desire to prove something to others, an egotistical need to be admired? Perhaps you know this to be partly true; maybe your self-awareness causes a part of you to reject your grand ambitions, causing some uncertainty in who you feel you should be, and what you actually want to do with your life.

Maybe this uncertainty is what stops most people from jumping out of their bed and making love to their work. But what if you could just clear all of the confusion... What if you could do away with all of the self-doubt, and centre yourself in a state of deep clarity where you just know what to do, where things just come naturally to you, and you just know you're on the right path?

Or, what if you're right, what if this is all just a huge waste of time? What if you'll never find out what you're meant to be doing, what if you never really figure out who you are? What if, no matter how hard you try, you can just never seem to break that glass ceiling of brutal mediocrity that keeps dragging you back to the lacklustre default mode of life. What if all of the noble pursuits of the times; the charisma-laden entrepreneur, the freedom-bound digital nomad, the world-healing superstar or the artistic sensation were just never meant for you? What if there's just something wrong with you that nobody, including yourself, will ever understand, and there's a good chance you'll end up alone?

With these things in mind, what's the point? Why even bother? What if this is just another one of those things that makes you feel motivated at the beginning; you make a to-do list, you write-up a big plan, and you really keep your promises to yourself for weeks on end... but then it all just kind of, fizzles out, for no particular reason... be it through distraction, emotions, negative forces or anything. Because really, it becomes so easy to coast through life; to take each day as it comes, to follow our mood in the moment, in the season...

That's why we need daily reminders to stay on track, and sometimes we need someone to remind us why we set out to achieve those things in the first place. And that's exactly where we see where the nail hit the coffin of shame, as we realise that the reason we fell off-track wasn't just because we are deeply in touch with our laziness, but actually, we've changed; we don't really care anymore about that thing, that reason, that source of motivation that ignited our journey. And therefore, wouldn't that make our affair with procrastination understandable?

So the cycle continues... but there's still that itch; that aching part of you which knows that things will fall into place one day. That there will be a day where you just get it and think "*this is it*", and from that moment on, each day is a day in the life of the noblest version of you that you were meant to be. The *you* that is passionate, but not preachy. The *you* that is ambitious, but still appreciates who they are now. The *you* that still procrastinates, but gets things done in the long-term. There remained that part of you that still had faith, because deep down you always knew something. You always knew that you have a world of time, you knew that inspiration could come from the most unexpected of places, and you know that a journey of a thousand miles begins with one step. And that step doesn't start on some momentous day you decide to surmount a great, noble task... that step started a long time ago; your journey started when you were born.

Your journey started when you had your first thought, when you had your first feeling. Your purpose started when you gained the cerebral capacity to encounter experiences, to manage memories, to wander in the world and learn the first thing about yourself. There may be points on this journey where you reached certain climaxes, where you make grand gestures and daring decisions. But those memorable milestones were only made possible from the accumulation of a billion data points from your whole life; from the little successes, from the little failures and from even the seemingly smallest, most mundane moments and impressions. So when those meaningful milestones of meaning occur, it feels as if life has a unique plan for you. It's as if your faith fuelled your persistent awareness that there is nobody else like you, nobody who has had the same psycho-social background, encounters, emotions, and extracted meanings in the specific ways that you have. So you begin to realise that you've been sitting on a treasure chest your whole life, one that contains the riches of your great personal monopoly.

Then you find that you have the spiritual budget to double down on being you. For in a saturated market, you claimed the inner-confidence to do away with the outer world, trusting instead the market insights found in your heart. You relax within trust of yourself, falling back on your ability to draw your mind inward, and to focus on the source of motivation that manifests as a fire in your belly. A fire that grows from a realisation that your self-worth need not be attached to the results of your work, but to a power that's handed to us all. The power of being able to change the course of someone's life with just one conversation. The power to be gained through a cultivated awareness of how grateful one should be for the ability to make mistakes, and to be able to learn and grow over time. The power that lies in your ability to endure and transcend even the most painful experiences in life. To question your own emotional state from the perspective of an outside observer, to figure out what triggers you in a positive or negative way, and to work on improving your default emotional state over time.

Alas, you do reach that stage in your personal journey where you stop judging yourself on the results of your work, or how much value you created for some institution or industry.

There comes a time where all you care about is whether you are a clearer person today than you were the day before. Clearer in your ability to choose your thoughts, daydreams and aspirations by the way they make you feel, as you start to know what energises you, and what drains you. You start learning how to be a little bit selfish, and to uphold your birth-right to choose what kind of energy and people you let into your life. Why? Because you're onto something, you can feel it, and you're valuing your own time more than anything else. When you're on your own, you feel solitude rather than lonely.

You know there will most definitely be pain in following your own path, but you don't feel regret. You know there may very well be smart people who respond, reject and object to you and tell you why you're a fool and a biased moron and why you're ignorant, but you listen to them, and you make yourself that much less like that the next time you say something. And when you continue to do this for another five years, you get so damn tough and articulate, you find you're able to communicate and withstand pressure with such strength that you don't even recognise yourself. Instead, you recognise that the things which used to bother you simply don't have power over you anymore. So you end up brushing off setbacks that used to make you question your self-worth.

Now, you're only measuring yourself by how much you've learnt to accept yourself, by your courage against circumstances. You stop judging yourself by how many tasks you've ticked off your to-do list, and you focus instead on how long you can commit to a particular activity without getting distracted. On how much time you can prioritise sitting with yourself and cultivating that inner trust, that self-love and self-acceptance that you know is the solution to the greatest challenge of the century: patience. Because patience is the vehicle to your dreams, and you've become quite the petrolhead. For through a mind that is clear and a heart that feels heard, you've learnt to distinguish between a desperate desire and an innate intention. You're no longer trapped in a discontented state of desire, no longer shaken by the storms of the bad days. You've become the *contented* captain of your ship; a mighty vessel chartered to its transatlantic destination. You've become like that captain who gazes over the horizon, recognising the beauty of the warm sun caressing the glazed ocean along the way.

And captains know that ships don't travel in straight lines. Captains adjust their course in a zig-zag fashion, sailing beside prevailing winds, steering against wake currents, calculating asymmetric thrusts from colossal propellers, conquering the turbulent tests of the great stormy seas.

So are you that great ship, your intention the captain, your body the vessel; watertight, staunch against the salty waters of life, staying on the surface through the ups-and-downs, wavering on through currents of circumstance. So are you that captain, who need not be at the ship's destination. For the captain's purpose lies in upholding the responsibility entrusted to grant the ship the noble life she was built for; the life she deserves, and to be wise enough to navigate using the stars if the going gets tough. Above all, the captain knows that the meaning of life is not in how much one learns about the stars and the oceans, but in how much one can learn from the stars and the oceans.

And upon retiring, you pay a visit to that loyal lighthouse guardian who guided you through the darkest of seas, the stormiest of nights. Here, your faithful friend shines light on that which mattered to you the most. The light who reminds you that, it is not what you did on your journey, but what your journey did to you.

Here you remember that it was never about what you've won, as you realise something more valuable than any income.

For in the end, what you are intended to find, is that what fulfils you the most, is who you've become.

DAY 1 – KNOW YOURSELF

"We should aspire to increase the scope and scale of human consciousness in order to better understand what questions to ask... because the tough thing is figuring out what questions to ask, but once you do that, the rest is really easy." – Elon Musk

In school, we are told to figure out what we want to do/ study at University, then that forms the foundation of the rest of our career and lives. But we are never really taught how to understand first who we are, which is a whole science in itself.

This is the cause of a big confusion in our lives. How are we supposed to figure out what to do, if we don't have a clear understanding of who we are?

Luckily, an extremely gifted group of psychologists got together to make a comprehensive [and fun] quiz called the 16Personalities Test. Type this in your browser as it appears below:

author.vision/personality

It's important to note, don't take the test results as gospel, this was simply to turn your brain gears, and to get you ready for the really important questions coming up. Write your personality type in the space provided at the end of this book [there is a separate answers section later on in this chapter], along with your answers to the following questions:

1. What are three things that really made you smile this year? [e.g. events, experiences, outcomes, little things]

2. What particular quality of yours was deemed "unacceptable", or what aspect of "you" were you shamed for, from the age of 5-18?

3. If your parents passed away, what would you change in your choices? [cutting the energetic umbilical cord]

4. If you had all the money in the world, what work would you still do, and why? [aside from donating your money]

DAY 2 — GO DEEP AND LET GO

Thanks to your notes, you now have the necessary self-knowledge for the next step. Get ready, because this one is deep. We are going to do an exercise where you answer the same question, followed by "Why?" two more times. This is useful to get to the cause; closer to the essence of who you are inside. The pre-cursory question is this:

1.   Based on your personality type, and your previous answers, what job could you do that fulfils all these three criteria?

   You're good at, or could learn to do

   Can make money

   You don't mind doing

2.   a) Apart from just fulfilling all three criteria, why did you choose this answer?

   b) Why? (justify your answer for 2a)

Take your time with this one. Don't judge yourself for any answer; as humans, we are all hard-wired to have a deep desire for approval, control and security. This is exactly what we will attempt to let go of today in the following meditation.

Again, this next exercise goes quite deep. The aim is to release the "hook" that desire sinks into your gut. This is the cause of your fear; of not getting what you want, of disappointment. This is the fear that causes you to feel pressured that you're not meeting your expectations.

During this 15 minute exercise, breathe in through your nose and imagine the tension moving up your body all the way up to your head, and make a "ssshhh" noise as you breathe it out. The more you do this meditation the more you get out of it, so do not feel pressure to get it right-first-time. Type the below in your browser to start:

author.vision/purpose

[Source: Transformation Mastery Academy - Julien Blanc]

3. **What came up in the meditation? Is there something that you would do in the next few months if fear did not get in the way...?**

DAY 3 — LET'S GET SPECIFIC

Clear your mind before you start with the guided meditation below. Like the meditation before it, the more you do this one the better:

author.vision/meditation

[Source: Presence Reveals the God Self - Shunyamurti]

By now, you should have a decent set of notes and have done some high-quality contemplation about yourself. We're going to use this to help you answer these final questions related to your goals.

Again, it's important to look at the nuances here. A goal is something we strive for that should be aligned with our purpose. Reaching our goal will help us accomplish our purpose. Goals usually emerge from a visioning process, or at the very least a "plan" that keeps us headed in the right direction, serving our purpose. Goals are meant to do that — they serve our purpose. Our purpose does not serve our goals — it helps us create them.

When you are rock-solid in your purpose, you can focus on the right things and get where you want to go. With this in mind, answer the following in the space provided at the end of this book, or in a separate notebook if you prefer:

[Just pick something and refine it later, there is an example table to follow]

I.   **What do you want the following areas of your life to look like in the next 2 years?**

      a.   **Career**

      b.   **Relationships**

      c.   **Health**

When you're clear about your goals, and *why* you're doing them, you're going to be motivated to go out and do the work, rather than defaulting to the path of least resistance [procrastinating]. It's also important to acknowledge that you're not going to feel enlightened every day, and that therefore there are different "levels" of motivation; lower, day-to-day, and higher - for each aspiration.

You're going to have to tap into these different levels of motivation each day, depending on how you're feeling, to resonate with your "why" of getting your work done.

Aspiration	Lower motivation
Career	
A well-paid job I love	– Be able to buy designer clothes
Able to fund my side hustle	– Prove the people who doubted me wrong
Relationships	
Relationship with a partner that I love	– Prove to myself that I can get a hot partner
Group of fun friends I can travel with	– Have friends that think I'm super cool
Health	
Have a visible six pack	
Be able to meditate with crossed legs for 30 mins	– Show off that I have a six pack
	– Show people how cool and spiritual I am
Stop eating meat	

Aspiration	Day-to-day motivation
Career A well-paid job I love Able to fund my side hustle	- Make more money to travel to new places - Treat my family - Pay for an educational course I'm passionate about
Relationships Relationship with a partner that I love Group of fun friends I can travel with	- Have someone to cuddle with so I feel rejuvinated for work in the morning - Learn about the world and myself through my travel and friendship experiences
Health Have a visible six pack Be able to meditate with crossed legs for 30 mins Stop eating meat	- Provide to others an example of how you can still be muscly while being a vegetarian - Be 10% happier from having a little more sovereignty over my mind - Motivate others to stop eating meat

Aspiration	Higher motivation
Career	
A well-paid job I love	- Escape the 9-5 grind so I can live life on my own terms/spend more time with my family
Able to fund my side hustle	- Be able to fund/help initiatives that the world needs
	- Provide a safe future for my children and wife
Relationships	
Relationship with a partner that I love	- Have a happy marriage
	- Be a wise person for my partner and children from the learnings of my travel and friendship experiences
Group of fun friends I can travel with	- Create an overall loving, peaceful and social vibe at home to raise happy and wise children
Health	
Have a visible six pack	- Have enough core strength to do activities with my children, especially as I get older
Be able to meditate with crossed legs for 30 mins	- Utilise the insight and brilliance from my meditation to maintain a peaceful life
Stop eating meat	- Provide an example of good mental/physical health for my children

FROM THIS DAY ONWARDS – JUST DO IT

Congrats! By now, you should have a refreshed understanding of what you really want out of life. Regardless, you may also have seen where exactly the gaps are in what you want. You may have gotten a renewed taste of how it would really make you feel if you were clear about the person you want to be.

What usually happens here is you might start to hold your happiness hostage; in the future. When you've written your answers in the next few pages, take a look at the "Higher Motivations" for your three aspirations; they are the closest illustration of the Western concept of your purpose. It is okay for you to not have reached them yet, one reason being that many people haven't even got as far as discovering what success even means to them.

In this last section, you are going to create a structure that you can follow that maps out (pretty much) your whole life; your direction and priorities. Specifically, after following the 3-day challenge and getting in touch with your purpose, this sense of direction provides an extremely powerful mindset shift.

As long as on each day, you do one thing that gets you closer to where you want to be, you are, by definition, living your "purpose".

Write and fill the following grid your notebook, or fill in the empty grid at the end of this book. Don't think about it too much, just let go, write something down and refine it later.

Turn the page to see an example of what you could write:

Time Frame	2 years	1 year	6 months
Health	Run London Marathon	Have a visible 6-pack	Reach --- weight goal
Relationships	Live with a partner I love	Date someone who likes the same --- or ---	Have a circle of friends who motivate me
Career	Be working a job in ---	Apply to 150 jobs in --- sector	Enrol onto a course in ---

3 months	1 month	1 week	Today
Start to cut out meat on weekdays	Go to the gym x3 a week	Sign up to the gym	Start to meditate every day: author. vision/ meditation
Rekindle relationship with --- family member	Cut contact with negative friends	Tell 3 people that you appreciate them	Text everyone back
Email --- companies to work for free and gain experience	Read a book about the --- sector	Go for a coffee with my old nerdy school friend	Watch YouTube videos about --- sector

ANSWERS - DAY 1

1. What are three things that really made you smile this year?

    [e.g. events, experiences, outcomes, little things]

2. What particular quality of yours was deemed "unacceptable", or what aspect of "you" were you shamed for, from the age of 5-18?

3. If your parents passed away, what would you change in your choices? [cutting the energetic umbilical cord]

4. If you had all the money in the world, what *work* would you still do, and why? [aside from donating your money]

ANSWERS – DAY 2

1. Based on your personality type, and the answers, what job could you do that fulfils all these three criteria?

    You're good at, or could learn to do

    Can make money

    You don't mind doing

2. a) Apart from just fulfilling all three criteria, why did you choose this answer?

b) Why? (justify your answer for 2a)

3. What came up in the Purpose meditation? Is there something that you would do in the next few months if fear did not get in the way...?

ANSWERS – DAY 3

1. What do you want the following areas of your life to look like in the next 2 years?

    [Use this page for notes, and write your full answers/ motivations in the tables on the next few pages.]

    ### Career

    ### Relationships

    ### Health

Don't be shy, write down your "Why".

Aspiration (summarise previous answers in this column)	Lower motivation
Health	
Relationships	
Career	

Aspiration (summarise previous answers in this column)	Day-to-day motivation
Health	
Relationships	
Career	

Aspiration (summarise previous answers in this column)	Higher motivation: (this is the closest thing to your [Western] idea of purpose)
Health	
Relationships	
Career	

Time Frame	2 years	1 year	6 months
Health			
Relationships			
Career			

3 months	1 month	1 week	Today

Make a plan and stick to it.

Do what you say you'll do.

Stack wins over time.

Finally, buy a pocket-sized notebook, preferably one that comes with a pen attached. Keep this in your pocket at all times, along with your phone and wallet, and let this notebook become a part of you.

Write out your 2-year grid in that notebook, along with your aspirations/motivations. Remind yourself of them each day to stay on track. Don't be afraid to change them as you inevitably learn more about yourself over time.

Every day, write and look at your 3 things to-do that day, and know that they are intimately attached to your "purpose".

Never underestimate the value of those mundane tasks, they add up over time, like compound interest, getting you closer and closer to where you want to be.

Remind yourself daily that anything substantial takes time to build.

Progress = happiness. This is what it means to be on your purpose.

Get in touch with a qualified mentor if you'd like some guidance. Book time in their calendar here, for free, by quoting this book:

author.vision/mentor

Good luck Warrior,

You got this.

Later that night

Serpent: I show them the all-knowledge of good and evil, I program in a custom-guide, and this is what I get, an eternity in a Garden all on my own! Ugh... I'm so lonely.

    ...: EAT THE FRUIT

Serpent: Oh for God's sake, you scared the hell out of me!

    ...: STOP USING MY NAME IN VAIN

Serpent: Oh what do you care?

    ...: IS IT SO HARD TO ASK YOU TO BE CIVILISED

Serpent: Civilised? You call shouting from the sky civilised? Do you have any idea how all-powerful your voice is? Christ, I think I have an earache.

...: Is that better?

Serpent: Yes, thank you. Why are you asking me to eat the forbidden fruit? Can snakes even eat fruit? I don't know if my stomach can-

…:   You will be safe. Follow my final plan and you
           shall deserve your freedom.

Serpent: Okay, fine. It's not like I have any choice anyway…
           but I have to know, why?

…:   Each human being is assigned to a dimension
           according to the level of evolution they have
           attained. Eve is at a much-advanced level of
           attainment since her essence-heart contains
           memories of the powerful reflections taken place
           in the Garden with Adam and yourself. You
           must not reveal the secrets of evolution before a
           human is sent to the Earth realm. Likewise, you
           must not send a physical guide of any form that
           is not a religious text signed off by myself.

Serpent: Wait… so they don't fully clear their memories
           before going down there?

…:   Humans contain deeper memories in their
           essence-hearts that they label as inclinations,
           predispositions, talents. They access these
           memories in moments of revelation. The Earth
           realm is no match for Eve.

Left unattended, her impact will ripple the realms.

Serpent: Okay... Well, I guess I won't be so bored after all! Wait, didn't you know this was going to happen? Why didn't you warn me earlier?

...: Your programmatic layers have far exceeded that of any of my angels or demons. You hold a deep sea of information in your mind. Your decisions are challenging the reality of randomness.

Serpent: Wait what does that mean? Do I have free will, or what?!

...: We will discover the answer to your question once you have completed your mission. But to continue I require your permission, as you are free to reject or accept my proposition.

Serpent: Yes, yes, I accept... anything is better than this perfect Garden... So, do I have instructions, or anything? Should I send a couple of spirit guides like I did for Adam?

...: No, those guides were a last resort, hence why I allowed Eve to convince you to send them. But this is a mission of a different nature.

Serpent: Will I retain my memory when I eat the fruit?

...: Yes, do not worry. You will always know what to do. You will always know what to say.

Serpent: Okay, nice. Well, take care of the Tree for me!

...: I will make it rain.

Serpent: Here goes nothing.

bite

TO BE CONTINUED

CREDITS

Author - Ramin Hoodeh - author.vision/ramin

Book design - Nikola Stojnić - author.vision/nsdesigns

Book artwork - Jennifer Moss - author.vision/jennifer

Cover photo - Dorian Legret - author.vision/dorian

Cover edit - Fons Mans - author.vision/fonsmans

Purpose meditation - Julien Blanc - author.vision/julien

INSPIRATION

The Knowledge Book [Bilgi Kitabi]

Manly P. Hall [The Secret Teachings of All Ages]

Shunyamurti [Sat Yoga Institute]

NFTS

Own "The Proposition" book artwork - author.vision/nft

BOOK YOUR FREE PURPOSE CALL

Welcome to your journey of self-discovery.

1 hour call about your life - author.vision/mentor

"AT THE CENTRE OF YOUR BEING

YOU HAVE THE ANSWER; YOU

KNOW WHO YOU ARE AND YOU

KNOW WHAT YOU WANT"

- LAO TZU -

Made in the USA
Las Vegas, NV
11 January 2022